SURVIVED
TO TELL *An Autobiography*

SURVIVED
TO TELL

The autobiography of
Edward Keonjian, Ph.D.

One of the pioneers of microelectronics,
the technology which transformed our daily lives.

A compelling and uplifting human story of survival, courage
and determination.

SUNSTONE PRESS

SANTA FE

Pictures 2 and 3 in chapter 1 were taken with permission of the author's family from the book by Vagharshag Elibekian published in Russian, Moscow, 1991.

Chapter 3 was adapted from the article "City of the Dead," published by the author under the pseudonym Eddie Kassian (in order to avoid intimidation by KGB agents) in the summer 1951 *Armenian Review*, a Boston-based quarterly literary publication.

Some material in chapter 4 was adapted from the article "Man Hunt," published by the author, also under the pseudonym Eddie Kassian, in the autumn 1949 *Armenian Review*.

Suntone books may be purchased for educational, business, or sales promotional use. For information please write: Special Markets Department, Sunstone Press, P.O. Box 2321, Santa Fe, New Mexico 87504-2321

FIRST EDITION

10 9 8 7 6 5 4 3 2 1

Library of Congress Cataloging in Publication Data:

Keonjian, Edward.
    Survived to tell: the autobiography of Edward Keonjian.—1st ed.
        p. cm.
    ISBN: 0-86534-252-0 (hc)
        1.Keonjian, Edward.   2. Microelectronics—Biography.   3. Armenians—United
States—Biography. I. Title.
TK140.K46A3   1996
621.381′ 092—dc20
    [B]   96-24330
                                                CIP

Published by   SUNSTONE PRESS
                    Post Office Box 2321
                    Santa Fe, NM 87504-2321 / USA
                    (505) 988-4418 / *orders only* (800) 243-5644
                    FAX (505) 988-1025

To my wife, Maria

For her encouragement, dedication, and tireless assistance
in all phases of the preparation of this book.

CONTENTS

ACKNOWLEDGEMENT

The author wishes to thank Mary Campbell for her valuable assistance in preparation of the manuscript. Her professional contribution is greatly appreciated.

PREFACE

It is February, 1942. German troops hold Leningrad, U.S.S.R., in the grip of history's cruelest siege—more than two million people will die before it is over in June 1944. Those who live through it and survive the long days of starvation and cold will be permanently scarred.

A lone woman walks through the devastated city, stepping carefully around the frozen bodies which litter every street. As she passes yet another makeshift common grave, she notices a slight movement from an upraised hand. She realizes that someone is still alive! Immediately she begins to dig out the man, who is nearly frozen.

Incredibly, she recognizes him as an old friend and brings him home. For the next couple of days she ministers to the comatose man as well as she can without heat or adequate food, water, or medicines. Finally, miraculously, he opens his eyes. At the age of thirty-two, he begins a new life.

I am that man, and this is the story of my many lives.

—Edward Keonjian
1996

ONE

*T*iflis is still one of the most beautiful cities in the world to me. It is called Tbilisi now, but I will always remember it as Tiflis, home of my heart, my birthplace. As I was growing up, Tiflis filled my senses and imagination—it was a magic place, with story-tellers on street corners, music pouring from the multi-colored houses with their laced balconies, and townspeople parading proudly through the narrow streets, showing off the latest fashions. Both men and women dressed beautifully and filled the city with color and romance. After one visit to Tiflis, Alexander Dumas said that he saw something delightful whichever way he turned. So did I.

Tiflis was not like the grimmer cities of northern Russia, where the sunlight was rationed and political arguments filled the air. The sun always shone in Tiflis, omnipresent flowers gave off clouds of perfume, and the cries of the yogurt vendors woke us to another enjoyable day— or so I remember it. The artist Vagharshag Elibekian painted many small portraits of old Tiflis in the rich colors it deserves. Long after you leave Tiflis, he wrote in his wonderful book, "it goes into the mind and soul."

This "little Paris of the Caucasus" is in Georgia, an independent state again now as it once was, before the Persians, before the Arabs and before the Mongols invaded it. Russia took it under its wing in 1801 and let it go in 1991—after nearly two centuries of dominance. They didn't let go easily, and that is part of the story of the Second Russian Revolution.

There is a reason so many peoples have wanted to rule Georgia and especially Tiflis: It is located on the strategic route between Poti on the Black Sea and Baku on the Caspian. Protected by the towering Caucasus Mountains, its climate is temperate and warm springs are plentiful. The 750-mile-long Kura River bisects the city and flows from Turkey to the Caspian Sea.

Tiflis has been a fortress city for almost 1500 years. King Vaktang Gorgasali declared the capital of Georgia in 458 A.D. and its stone walls completed early in the sixth century. In the thirteenth century Marco Polo wrote that he found "a beautiful town, Tipilisi by name, surrounded by settlements and a multitude of strongholds."

Part of the magic of Tiflis is its weave of Middle East and European cultures. Slavic, Georgian, Armenian, Turkic, and Persian. Their music, literature, food, religion, and amusements blended together, and although there were distinct divisions between the European side of town and the Asian side of town we moved freely between the two. There were not only several languages heard in the streets, there were three alphabets seen in the signs on the shops and kiosks: Armenian, Georgian, and Russian. We children had to learn them all.

The Georgians are known for their longevity. Perhaps it is because of the beautiful mountain climate or because they eat so much yogurt or because they generally do not work too hard or a combination of these things. Whatever the reason, most of them live a very long time. A story was told that Stalin heard about a man in Tiflis who was celebrating his 130th birthday. He decided to send a delegation to congratulate him on this remarkable feat. The delegation asked the old man what present he'd like for being the oldest person in the world. He answered that he was too old to have any wishes and only wanted to be left alone.

"Oh, no," replied the head of the delegation. "You can't refuse a present from our beloved comrade Stalin. He will take it as an insult."

"In that case," said the old man, "please find for me my son, Seto, who by now should be one hundred years old. It would be the best present for me. However, I'm afraid it will be practically impossible to find him after thirty years."

"Do not worry!" said the head of the delegation. "No one can disappear in the Soviet Union. We will find him, dead or alive."

Two months later the delegation came again to the old man, bringing with them twelve men. Among them was his son.

"Now," said the head of the delegation, "can you recognize your son?"

"Of course," said the old man, going to his son and embracing him. "This is him!"

Everyone was astonished. "How could you recognize your son after so many years?" asked the head of the delegation.

"Very simple," the old man said. "By his overcoat."

My parents were Armenian. Armenia had at one time been a very large and independent kingdom. After repeated invasions, it had sought out the protection of the more powerful Russia. Armenia was one of the first nations in the world to adopt Christianity as its state religion in 301 A.D. Muslims moved into neighboring Anatolia (Turkey), however, converting that kingdom and spreading prejudice against Christians. My grandfather, a jeweler from Erzurum named Martiros Keonjian, was to feel the sting of that persecution in 1905. He fled to Georgia and safety with my father, Mkrtich. They were some of the lucky ones. Thousands of Armenians who stayed in Turkey were slaughtered in the massacre of 1915, the first genocide in modern history.

After he arrived in Tiflis, my father rented a small room in the basement of a house belonging to a wealthy Armenian family, the Salinians. As fate would have it, there was a beautiful young daughter in the family named Satenik. She and the young refugee fell in love.

Satenik's brothers were furious when she announced her intention to marry my father. They did not want their youngest sister to marry a penniless refugee. They threatened to kick him out of the house. But before that could happen, the couple eloped and fled to Kharkov in the Ukraine, 1,200 miles from home. There they attended the university from which both eventually graduated with medical degrees.

My father remains a shadowy figure to me. A handsome man and a dapper dresser, it is easy to see how he captivated my mother.

However, he did not marry only Satenik—he tied himself to the large Salinian family, with its layers of brothers, sisters, cousins, aunts, uncles, nephews, and nieces. It must have been very difficult for him to compete with so many relatives who thought they knew better than he how to live his life.

We were proud of being Armenian rather than Georgian. It seemed to us that Armenians were the workers, the builders, and artists, while Georgians, in the eyes of Armenians, were too easy-going and fun-loving. However, my great-grandfather Giko Salinasvilli, was a Georgian and, in fact, was born a serf. In general, in all Russian provinces as well as in Russia proper, serfs were more like indentured servants than slaves. Their labor was owned by their lord, but not their lives. Families were usually kept together—not divided up and sold as American slaves were—because they worked the land together. Nevertheless, they were destined to serfdom forever, unless their masters granted them freedom. That is what happened to Giko.

The Georgian Prince Aslan Orbeliani was in debt to the government for unpaid taxes. A part of his estate was auctioned off. Among his belongings and real estate were the family of fifty-year-old Giko Salinasvilli, his house and the land on which it stood. Maria, the daughter of an Armenian retired major general, Count Simonich, bought all the above for four hundred silver rubles.

Giko must have been brighter or cleverer or more ingratiating than most serfs, because Maria soon petitioned the government to free him and his family. Her petition was granted and "by a special decree in the name of the Tsar Nicholas I" on November 12, 1846, Giko's family was granted freedom from serfdom. This was fifteen years before the general emancipation of Russian serfs in 1861, and seventeen years before the slaves were freed in America. With freedom, Giko changed his name from Salinasvilli to Salinian, in gratitude to the Armenian woman who gave him liberty.

Giko's house was described in the petition as a typical serf's cottage, barely more than a roof and four walls to protect his family from the weather. It was a one-room dwelling made of rocks and bricks covered with dirt. Measuring 12.6 meters by four meters, it had a dirt floor and a wooden ceiling. It was surrounded by other such huts and had a garden—probably equally small.

In this primitive hut, for which they paid a rent of two silver rubles a year, lived Giko, his wife Catherine (referred to in the family as "fat Catherine" to distinguish her from the other Catherines who appeared), and their four children: Vaso, Georgi, Stephan, and Camelia. Georgi, who would become my grandfather, was fifteen years old in 1846 when he was given the gift of freedom. He was young enough to consider the life ahead of him (it would not be correct to assume he "planned a career," as his descendants would do), but old enough to have missed an education. Possibly he could read, write, and do sums, but beyond that he must have been fairly ignorant. Yet the flame of intellectual curiosity may have flickered within him—it certainly burned brightly in later generations.

Or perhaps that particular set of values and genes came from my grandmother, "thin Catherine," an Armenian woman of high breeding and considerable wealth. How did these two get together—the former serf-turned-merchant and the well-born lady? It is a mystery to me, but speaks of a certain sense of democracy that must have been at work in the Caucasus. Thanks to her, the Salinians were taken out of poverty and into gentility.

I did not know my grandfather Georgi on my mother's side. He had died before I was born, but I remember my grandmother Catherine as bedfast, always ill. Perhaps she was crippled by a form of arthritis. She liked me to crawl into bed with her as a child, calling me "my dear medicine." Did I give her warmth? Or perhaps she hoped to drain off some of my vitality, giving her the energy to get her through the day. Fortunately, whether through her own wealth or the money my grandfather made as a merchant, she was able to spend her last years surrounded by servants who cared for her.

Georgi and Catherine had eight children, four boys and four girls, spread out over twenty years. My mother was the youngest and so the most protected. The family prospered and thrived, remaining close as it expanded. They could not punish Satenik forever. My parents' exile ended sometime after I was conceived. Her marriage was forgiven, and we all arrived back in Tiflis just before I was born, although I do not remember that particular trip.

I arrived in August, nine years into the twentieth century. My parents gave me the name of Eduard, which for a strange reason was very common in Tiflis, much like John or Robert in the United States. In fact, almost every tenth child on our street was named Eduard! We all were given the nickname Edik. Soon after I was born I was baptized in the Armenian Gregorian Church, a part of the Eastern Orthodox tradition.

We lived in a large apartment on the second floor of a three-story building in a prestigious area near the river. The house where the Russian poet Mikhail Lermontov lived during his exile in Tiflis was not far. Here he wrote *The Demon* and *Mtsyri*. Pushkin and Gribaedov also chose Tiflis as their city of exile. Our apartment was light and airy, with furniture of light wood and large windows. Its most prominent feature was its balcony overlooking the street, from which we could watch the life of the city.

These large balconies with their delicately carved pillars and intricately engraved canopies and handrails gave a distinctive mark to the city. Residents sat for hours on them, drinking fragrant tea with lemon, playing cards, chatting, and most of all, watching the street. The streets in Tiflis were very narrow (many have since been widened) and tortuous. It was said that you couldn't see from one end of a block to another because of the twists and turns. Their narrowness was also legendary. The story was often repeated of a merchant hurrying along who got stuck on the sidewalk behind an abundant matron taking her time meandering down the street. "Humph!" he muttered. "Why didn't the city fathers measure the hips of the residents before they built the sidewalks!"

We woke each morning to a multitude of pleasant smells, the perfume of fresh flowers—magnolias, jasmine, lilacs, pear blossoms—and the aromas of fresh Georgian bread. *Shotis puri* is the long bread and *chureki* is round, baked in the ancient tradition. Dough was placed on the vertical walls of hot pit ovens called *thornis*. It had to be made of pure semolina to be able to adhere to the hot walls of the pit. After it was baked for twenty minutes or so, it was scraped off. Spread with fresh butter, it was heavenly. We also ate a paper-thin rolled bread called *lavash*, which dates back four thousand years. It is still made primarily by Armenian bakers and is now found throughout the world.

Each morning at six my father shopped for food in Gorgasali Square, just across the Kura River. Even at that hour the market was teeming with shoppers looking for bargains among the stalls. Here there were all kinds of vegetables, grapes, olives, pomegranates, figs, dates, candied fruits, cheese, meat, breads, spices, tea, Turkish coffee, wine in sheepskins, vodka, strings of garlic, and another Tiflis specialty: "sausages" made of prunes, nuts, and molasses. The intermingling aromas, with their promise of delicious meals, made my mouth water. Dogs nosed around the vendors, looking for tidbits of food, their mouths watering as well.

Other stalls offered clothes, bolts of silk, kitchen utensils, and crafts, such as shoemaking and barbering. Chinese merchants sold paper lanterns and small wooden whistles. Voices rang out as neighbors recognized each other, vendors shouted out advertisements, customers argued for the best price—all in Georgian, Armenian, or Russian. Despite the cacophony, the market was not chaotic. There was a definite order in the presentation of wares and in the sales transactions. In earlier times, camels laden with silks and brocade from the East or carpets from the West added their snorts, while donkeys brayed and oxen bawled.

My father loved to bargain for every item he purchased, especially meat, and paid for his purchases with large folded rubles. Following behind him was my elderly Nanny with a string bag full of food. Nanny was a tall and thin Ossetian, from an ancient peoples of Eastern Persia, the Alans. She never learned to speak any of the languages we could speak—Armenian, Russian, or Georgian—and I don't know how she managed to communicate with us. She was a part of the Salinian family for over forty-five years—she raised my mother—so somehow she learned to understand our needs and we hers.

After Father and Nanny came home, we'd eat our breakfast in the large dining room. Often we had fresh bread with feta cheese, eggs, Georgian tea, and fruit. Sometimes breakfast would be interrupted by a loud shout of "*Matsoni!*" (yogurt) and Mother would go to the balcony to negotiate with the street vendors who walked up and down the cobblestone streets. When a suitable price was agreed upon, Mother would throw down the coins and the vendor would leave his eggs or yogurt inside the door. It was up to me to go downstairs and bring then back up for the family.

My mother was a tall slender woman with dark, expressive eyes. I always thought of her as an intellectual—she had a very quick, insightful mind—yet she was also loving and warm. In my earliest years I loved to climb into her comfortable lap and listen to her musical voice read me stories. She could be passionately angry, as well as tender, and never backed away from an argument. For as long as I can remember my parents argued. They had, as I analyzed it, two major problems. One was her family, which wanted to oversee our every move, and the other was his interest in young women, particularly in the young Russian servant girls that my mother hired. It seemed that every six months or so one would be dismissed and another hired, probably with the promise of "Never again!"—a promise that was quickly forgotten. My favorite cousin Flora was often called in to mediate their arguments and probably helped to keep them together. Much later, Flora's daughter Anna, a medical doctor, had the same function of mediator among all the other relatives. It was a family tradition.

My father gradually withdrew from my mother and her accusations, becoming more and more involved with backgammon or *nardy*, which was played with ardor in Turkey. Almost every evening he'd escape to a friend's house, for he rarely played at our home with his heavy, beautifully carved set. Consequently, I did not know him well. In fact, I felt somewhat closer to several of my uncles and cousins. I did my share of escaping the home atmosphere, too, and there were several Salinian relatives who welcomed me.

One of my favorites was Uncle Amazasp Ambartsumian. He had a wonderful library, bought from some estate. Among the books were those by James Fennimore Cooper, Jack London, and Mark Twain. These rugged Americans captivated my heart and I passionately wanted to be not a cowboy, but an Indian. So intoxicated did I become by these tales of the Far West, that I made myself an Indian outfit, stealing the tail feathers of the neighborhood roosters.

Digging around in the discarded articles in the trash bin, I found an old pipe that became a peace pipe, a rope that became a lasso, and parts for a tomahawk. With borrowed cosmetics, I painted my face and retired to the attic for a pow-wow. If my war whoops and dancing did not call enough attention to myself, the smoke from the peace pipe did. It was only a small fire, but it was enough to put an end to my Indian activities. Sadly I realized I would have to wait until I was grown to go to America and save the redskins from the pale faces.

I read more than American tales, of course, and my mother encouraged my enthusiasm, being an avid reader herself. I went through all the Armenian, Russian, and European classics at an early age and thrilled to the adventures of the Count of Monte Cristo and the Three Musketeers, as well as the more intellectual stories of Ivan Turgenev and Leo Tolstoy. Tolstoy begain his first important novellas—*Childhood, Hadji Murat*, and *The Cossacks*—while in Tiflis, waiting to be enrolled in the Caucasus Army.

Many of the grandchildren of former serf Georgi Salinian were well-educated and mentally quick. My cousin Viktor Ambartsumian, son of the lawyer and book collector, became an internationally known astrophysicist with scores of degrees and honors. In 1961 he was elected president of the International Astronomical Union. He still is a member of the French, German, and other Academies of Science, and for many years was president of the Armenian Academy of Sciences, until his retirement in 1992.

Shakespeare was admired in Tiflis and his plays were frequently staged. We Armenians loved the works of the poet Sayat Nova, who in the fourteenth century gave up the sensual life for the austere life of a monk when his passion for a noblewoman was thwarted. One of

Georgia's greatest writers was Shota Rustaveli, during the reign of Queen Tamara in the twelfth century, who wrote an epic poem, *The Knight in the Tiger's Skin*. Even today pieces of that work are memorized in Georgian schools.

Rustaveli Avenue, the main street of Tiflis, was only a few blocks from our house. This was a street for strolling, wide enough for several ladies in their long skirts, twirling their parasols and flicking their veils and corkscrew curls (discreetly, of course), hoping to catch the eyes of the handsome young men in their Prince Albert coats and beaver hats who thoughtfully studied the shop windows, as if Turkish daggers or *arkhaluks* (soft boots) were all they had on their minds. Automobiles came to Tiflis not long after I was born, but horse-drawn carriages, ox carts, and donkey caravans were much more numerous. Occasionally a huge camel would lumber down the street, urged along by his driver. The sight never failed to thrill me.

Once, a fourteen-foot Bengal tiger was shot on the street. Apparently, he had wandered all the way from the Persian steppes. We schoolchildren were taken to the museum to see the display of his magnificent long corpse.

The streets of Tiflis were alive—and it seemed that the whole world marched before us as we watched: Chinese and Persian merchants and Georgian-Armenian musicians playing traditional *zurna*. The circus often came to town. I especially enjoyed going to watch the wrestlers there, maybe because I was so scrawny. A masked wrestler captured my allegiance when he promised not to remove his mask until he was defeated. Week after week I watched him pin his opponents and cheered when he was declared the winner. At last he was defeated and, true to his word, he removed his mask. I don't know what I expected, but there looking at us was an ordinary man. It was a great disappointment.

The *kinto* was an important part of Georgian street life. He was a kind of all-around entertainer—singer, comedian, master of ceremonies. No wedding or family party could be celebrated without him. Also plying his trade on the streets was the *musha*. The musha was an old man who made a living carrying heavy furniture on his back from place to place—tables, sofas, and even pianos! Somehow he had learned to distribute the weight, using a heavy, padded pillow on his back. Unbelievably, he could climb two or three sets of stairs with these loads.

Music was so much a part of Tiflis that I cannot see a picture of the old town without hearing notes of an accordion or hurdy gurdy. The great operatic bass, Feodor Shalyapin (or Chaliapin) once said, "I was born twice. In Khazan I opened my eyes to life and in Tbilisi, to music."

For a kopek, a singer would serenade you or play his guitar while you looked soulfully into the eyes of your beloved. Piano music and vocal selections streamed out of the houses. It seemed to me that everyone, except me, was practicing something. And there were several conservatories in town, one begun by Vano Saradzhishvili, the celebrated tenor. Tchaikovsky found inspiration in Tiflis, beginning *The Sleeping Beauty* and *The Queen of Spades* here. One of the city's most celebrated choreographers was George Balanchivezde, known in the world today as Balanchine.

Live birds, especially canaries and parrots, were sold on the streets of Tiflis. Lambs, too. These lambs are well known the world over for their thick and heavy wool. I was given two as pets when I was very young and given as well the responsibility of taking them to pasture on Mount David. They became very dear friends to me, and comforted me when I felt lonely. I had a blanket made from their wool. It has warmed me for three-quarters of a century, through illness and despair. Even today, it is my special comforter.

About once a month we went to the baths. There were several of these in the Asiatic or Eastern sector of town, which took advantage of the hot springs, rich in hydrogen sulfide, that arise inside Mount Tabori. The best known was the Orbeliani Baths and frequently we went to that one. This trip was not simply for recreation, but for a cleaning down to the marrow and I dreaded it. First my father packed the carriage with food and drink—for this was a day-long excursion—and then reluctantly I crawled in beside him. The baths we attended were housed in a large stone building with sunken marble tubs. Possibly, soaking in the water was a treat for adults and perhaps it contributed to the general health and longevity of Georgians, but for years I associated it only with pain. Pushkin wrote about these baths, "I have never in life, neither in Russia or Turkey, come across anything more sumptuous than the baths in Tiflis." Alexi Tolstoy compared them to the Roman baths.

The baths were segregated by sex and for the first several years of my life I went with my mother into the women's area. This stopped abruptly when I was about eight. One day I was innocently enjoying the sight of so much female nudity. Perhaps one of the women misinterpreted my boyish stare, for she angrily complained to my mother. Admittedly I was tall for my age, but I certainly did not have whiskers on my face at that age as she alleged. At any rate, I was summarily dismissed from that pool of abundant beauty and sent to be with my father.

The bath ritual in the men's section began with a simple cleaning. Hot water spewed out of the mouths of two marble lions, keeping the water bubbling. After a short period of soaking, we were told to leave the water for the scrubbing room. Here we were scrubbed—scoured!—from head to foot with a very rough material called *kissa*. The scrubbing was engineered not merely to take the dirt off the skin, but to take the skin off the boy, at least the first layer or two. When we were sufficiently raw, we were wrapped in Turkish towels and given a cup of tea.

The tea was not enough to take my mind off my stinging, smarting body, and it was days before I healed enough to dress without yelping with pain. Men like my father, who were very hairy and yet aspired to a more romantic, hairless body, could also subject themselves to a depilatory process, probably waxing. Fortunately, I was not old enough to be given that option. I can still hear the cries of my father as the attendant wiped the depilatory solution off his chest.

Later, when I was a high school student, I liked to come to the baths just to soak in the hot water (without the *kissa*), especially after a grueling exam. Many of us students found the baths a way to relax totally, away from parents, teachers, and girls.

Perhaps because of my experience with appreciating feminine beauty in the baths, when I was about ten, I decided to become an artist. I invited a neighbor's daughter to be my model. She was twelve and readily agreed to pose in the nude. I was absorbed in my sketching when I suddenly noticed the paper darkening. The shadow of my father was blocking my light. Next, I felt the sting of a slap. Within seconds the girl had grabbed her clothes and was on her way home, screaming. After that my father never missed an opportunity to refer to me sarcastically as "my son, the great artist." I did not pick up a sketch pad again.

If art was not my calling, perhaps music was. My mother was an accomplished pianist and tried to teach me to play. She thought that since I had long fingers as she did, I would also have her talent. Alas, I did not and after a few months she gave up her instruction.

I felt that I had disappointed my parents with my artistic ability and I also disappointed them with my academic ability. I was an indifferent student and graduated with difficulty from the strict Armenian elementary school.

But that did not mean my mind was not eager to learn! It was busy all the time, observing, thinking, and most of all trying to figure out how things worked. I loved to tinker, especially with electrical gadgets. I was fourteen years old when the first radio transmitter came to Tiflis. I was in heaven! I felt instantly that this infant technology would be my destiny and I wanted to learn everything about it. I built the first radio set in town, long before the invention of vacuum tubes. I had to improvise my own batteries, combining various chemicals, and I strung an enormously long wire—600 feet or more—over the roofs of several buildings in order to have a long enough antenna to receive radio signals. One of my neighbors thought I was trespassing and called the police. After my angry father bailed me out of jail, all I could think about was getting back to my crystal set and I didn't even listen to his reproaches. When I finally picked up some faint signals, my world suddenly, dramatically expanded far beyond Tiflis. The programs I received were amateurish at first—news accounts, weather reports, and a few musical shows, mainly in Russian.

Many years later in America, I met someone from Tiflis who remembered this young boy who was "radio mad" and who was always stringing his wires around.

To finance my radio set, I had to earn the funds, because my parents did not believe in giving me pocket money. My plan was to buy candies wholesale and sell them piece by piece to our guests who came to play cards with my parents. The winner usually bought all the left-overs; otherwise I would have eaten them myself. I was embarrassed by my sales career and never tried it again, finding other ways to make money.

Still, my parents were not impressed with my tinkering ability and it seemed that no matter what I did I could not please them. One day I decided to run away from home (or perhaps I was only looking for adventure). I had just received a new pair of shoes and decided to use them. I hitchhiked to the nearest seaport, which was Batumi, on the Black Sea, 150 miles from Tiflis. There I climbed on board the first ship anchored in the dock. I was sure that every ship was going to America and I would go with it! I hid under a canvas and sat there all night with my heart in my mouth—even forgetting how hungry I was—waiting for the ship to sail.

Somehow I fell asleep toward dawn and woke up when we were on the open sea, or so I thought. It wasn't long before I was discovered, and then I learned that I was only on a cargo ship that shuttled between two ports about three miles apart. There was not much adventure in that! The kind ship's captain fed me breakfast and then called my parents, who were mortified. I still can feel my father's hand on my behind. I was not completely cured of my desire to travel, but I did hold it in check for a while, at least until I could do it on my own terms.

Perhaps if I had been interested in my parents' medical careers, we would have become closer. Physicians did not have the prestige then that they do today in the United States, but still, they were regarded as professionals. My parents' office was in our home, as was the custom then, and they saw patients only during set times, except when there was an emergency. They also dispensed medicines. However, I never felt a part of their professional lives and never showed any curiosity about patient care, so that avenue was closed to me.

There is a saying that physicians should never doctor members of their own families. I believe it. When I was about eight years old, I contracted a severe case of diarrhea, probably from the untreated drinking water. My parents' remedy was to starve the sickness and me. They kept me on a strict diet consisted of boiled water and practically no food whatsoever. As a result, after about three weeks I was a living skeleton, looking as if I could die at any moment.

Fortunately for me, by sheer accident a medical colleague of my parents, Dr. Zargarian, came to visit them. Seeing my condition, he was horrified and immediately prescribed steak, *kasha* (a very popular buckwheat porridge), eggs, chicken, and vegetables. Thus my life was saved. Although my parents' treatment sounds unnecessarily cruel, it was not unusual for physicians at that time to experiment with extremes in diet.

My life became even more difficult at home when my brother Paruyr was born in 1917. Gradually I found myself in the periphery of my family's life. My mother no longer had time to read books to me. My father hardly spoke to me. I thought this was because he found me unconventional and difficult. Perhaps a better analysis would be that *he* was unconventional and difficult!

As I mentioned earlier, my father's father was a jeweler and after he fled from Turkey to Tiflis, he set up a small shop. One day he dropped dead from a heart attack while working. My father knew that his father had considerable gold in his possession and searched the shop for it repeatedly without luck. He even dug under the floor of the shop, two feet into the ground, but there was still no gold.

When the shop was closed, my grandfather's furniture was brought to our house. We gradually sold it off, taking it to the nearest market. Soon only one very heavy, ugly old table was left, which no one wanted to buy. For weeks our nanny struggled with that table, carrying it to the market and then carrying it home again. One day as she arrived home, she became so disgusted with it that she slammed one leg on the steps of the house. Behold! A shower of gold coins burst from the broken leg. It was like the well-known Russian story, "The Twelve Chairs," when the last unsold chair was broken to reveal the treasure hidden in its upholstery.

The unexpected find—for we had given up hope—made my father instantly rich. Now his main concern was hiding the gold from potential thieves, who were in abundance in town. He was especially worried that one of our neighbors who witnessed the event would tell everyone what he had seen. My father immediately gave him a handful of coins to silence him.

For his next step, my father was very clever. He ordered a gynecological chair with a heavy cast iron base that was hollow. He filled the cavity with the gold coins, and although we were continuously visited by robbers looking for the gold, no one found it. My father became obsessed with the chair and refused to separate himself from it. We had to take it with us to the mountains in the summer, where my father continued his practice among the summer residents in Borjomi. Perhaps he took it with him to the grave, or perhaps my younger brother, who lived with him in Moscow, got it, for I never learned what happened to it.

Our excursions required much planning and preparation. We packed the ox-cart to overflowing and spent a long day traveling to get to our cabin, where we'd spend a few weeks. For shorter day trips we used the funicular to take us to a picnic spot on Mount David. At the top were tea houses and a merry-go-round. From there we could see the orchards and vineyards that surrounded Tiflis.

As I moved into adolescence, I was a lonely child without the support of loving parents. Tall, stringy, giraffe-like, with an enormous head of bushy hair, I was very awkward and shy, a loner who lived in his own world and dreamed of building great radios. My schoolmates took advantage of my awkwardness and I was constantly beaten up by aggressive boys who were smaller. Finally I made a decision to stop the onslaught. I became convinced that I must build up my muscles and become strong enough to fight back.

I found a Russian translation of a famous book written by a German by the name of Mueller, who described how he, once weak and shy, had become a sort of "Tarzan." I took his advice to heart and started exercising vigorously in front of the big mirror in our entrance hall. In a short while our apartment became a kind of gym, despite my parent's disapproval, with all sorts of primitive gadgets to build my physique. (Vladimir Nabokov's father used the same book and regime in 1907, when he was in solitary confinement in a Russian prison.)

As soon as I felt strong enough, I challenged the most vicious of the boys to a fight. It took place in an abandoned shed. The entire class came to witness my downfall, but I won! No one was more surprised than I. After that miracle, I was safe from any further humiliation at school. Unfortunately, my school work did not benefit from this episode and I barely squeaked through high school.

My high school was all-male, as was usual at that time. It was also usual to have only male instructors. Once, to our delight, we found that biology was going to be taught by a young, beautiful woman. Emma couldn't have been more than twenty-two years old.

Our entire class instantly fell head over heels in love with her. We began bringing field glasses to class with us so we could stare more closely at her. When she asked us to put them away, we'd say we were near-sighted and needed them "to better understand biology." Jealous of any part of her life that didn't include us, we began watching her every move. When she was ill, we organized a vigil outside her house. As soon as we learned that one of our male teachers had visited her, we confronted him and demanded he stop seeing her. Being the object of so much passionate love was very difficult on Emma. She quit her job. It was the saddest day of our young lives.

I was twelve years old when the American movie star Mary Pickford visited Tiflis on her tour of Russia. All the boys in my class were excited about seeing her. We'd been fascinated by her motion pictures, especially the edge-of-your-seat train chases and the romances with Douglas Fairbanks. After she left, I wrote to her in Hollywood, expressing my admiration. I was thrilled to receive a reply and an autographed photograph. I carried it around with me for weeks and showed it to everyone who looked in my direction. "See! The famous and beautiful Mary Pickford wrote to me!"

Our clumsiness in romantic affairs was also evident in a very odd game called *nachunaki* that we played with the neighborhood girls, who probably didn't even know they were part of a game. We boys dared each other to touch a girl's bare elbow or arm. Those who could document these touches (through the testimony of a witness), could "sell" the touch to a less courageous boy for a few candies. The most daring boys were able to accumulate many touches and lots of candy. It was considered that a touch was good for twenty-four hours only. It was cheating to sell yesterday's touch today.

At the age of sixteen I fell desperately in love with my first cousin Margo. The daughter of my uncle Vaso, she was exquisitely beautiful, eight years older than I, an unobtainable twenty-four. Every chance I could, I visited Uncle Vaso, only half-listening to his stories while I stared open-mouthed at the beautiful Margo. Occasionally she would allow me to kiss her cheek and I would practically swoon, being close enough to her to smell her dusky perfume and feel the softness of her skin.

But this world of romance could not last. Such sweet memories are made sweeter by contrast with the grim years ahead of us. We could not know, sitting on our flower-bedecked balconies and sipping Georgian tea with lemon as we watched the sun set behind the mountains, how full of horror life would become.

Neither World War I nor the Russian Revolution of 1917 really affected our lives in Tiflis. Without much upheaval, the Georgian Social-Democratic Party had taken over Georgia in 1917 and declared its independence from Russia. But we were not aware of any changes in the city. They ruled until February 25, 1921, when Red Army troops (*Bolsheviks*) moved in. Within a month Soviet power was established in the whole of Georgia. Because of disturbances in the streets, we were escorted to and from school.

We schoolchildren thought the Revolution meant we would have complete freedom and we wouldn't have to listen to our teachers. We began boycotting our classes as a lark. Later, the director of our school and other intellectuals that we admired were arrested, held in prison, and some of them shot. Tiflis was going through the process of "intellectual cleansing" and we lost many of our prominent citizens. It was a sad and frightening time.

My family was also in upheaval, as my parents divorced during my last year in high school. My father went to Moscow with my young brother and dropped out of my life. I stayed for a while with my mother, but we began arguing more and more. She was insisting that I follow in her footsteps and choose a medical profession.

I had no intention of doing so. My interest was in electrical engineering, just as it had been when I put together my first radio. After attending one year at the Georgia Polytechnical Institute in Tiflis, I decided to pursue my higher education in Leningrad. My mother was so opposed, she refused to give me any financial support either for my trip or for my education. Our parting was painful.

Not having a penny in my pocket, and with Russia still reeling from the effects of the Soviet Revolution, I climbed on board a railroad train. My plan was to get all the way to Leningrad, 1,600 miles away, where I would enroll in Russia's most prestigious scientific institution, the Leningrad Electrotechnical Institute.

TWO

*A*t the age of seventeen I was on my own. I knew that in leaving Tiflis I was making a break with my childhood and my family, and it was not without some trepidation and sorrow that I made the move. However, I also knew that I wanted to be a part of the exciting new world of radio waves. The idea of being able to reach anywhere in the world with electromagnetic signals opened up technological possibilities that the generation before me had never dreamed of. I wanted to learn, to experiment, to tinker!

So I started out in the summer of 1928, hoping to reach Leningrad in time for the beginning of fall classes at the Electrotechnical Institute (LETI). Since I could not afford to buy a ticket, early one morning I climbed aboard a train in the Tiflis railway station and hid from the conductor. He didn't discover me for many miles. When he did, he chased me off and I simply waited for another train to sneak aboard.

Our route went first through Baku and then turned north. As we moved farther away from the Caucasus, great plains stretched out before me with miles of flax and sunflowers. For a while we were on the edge of Russia's great "breadbasket," where most of its grain was grown. Then, as we approached Moscow, we entered the birch forests that Tolstoy loved, where wolves prowled at night. I stopped briefly in Moscow to get some rations and a few rubles from the local office of the Students Union, an organization which gave assistance (minimal, to be sure) to students on the road. North of Moscow, the light became thinner and the wind chillier. The vegetation changed again, as we approached the Gulf of Finland, to pale green grasses and scrawny trees.

I knew no one in Leningrad and when I reached it at last, I had to find a place to live right away. Fortunately, I was able to secure lodging in the dormitory for Institute students, where there was also an inexpensive cafeteria. And I found a series of odd jobs which allowed me to live a bit above the subsistence level.

At last I was admitted to the Institute, where the great Alexander Popov, whom Russians consider as the inventor of radio, was the first elected president. I had no particular problem entering that school because, as an Armenian I was considered a minority in the Soviet Union. At that time the government practiced a sort of "affirmative action" policy, giving minorities some preferential treatment over the ethnic Russians. In the later years that policy was abandoned in favor of academic excellence only. Many of my credits from the Georgia Polytechnic Institute were accepted, allowing me to advance quickly. My excitement for learning was only slightly dimmed by the drastic experiment that was then being conducted in socialistic education. European education traditionally assembled a crowd of students into a large hall where a professor lectured and occasionally answered questions. But at the Institute, our large auditoriums were compartmentalized into 8' x 8' cubicles for three to four students who were organized into "brigades." Our small group had to study together, but only one of us was responsible for passing the examinations. I suppose we were to learn solidarity this way, if we all worked toward the goal of achieving success for one, but this was an odd novelty and in two years the procedure was dropped.

Higher education in the Soviet Union was of two major types: A university education was general and covered many disciplines, much like a liberal arts education in the West; an institute education was geared to the specific requirements of a particular industry. There were then more than 100 institutes in the Soviet Union and about twenty in Leningrad—institutes in meteorology, rail transportation, medicine, mining, and pedagogy, for instance. The Polytechnical Institutes were engineering schools. LETI, which was located on Pesochni Street across

from the botanical gardens, had been founded in 1886 and was originally named for Tsar Alexander III. After 1917 it was renamed for
Lenin. It is now called Electrotechnical University. In 1930 another
institute, the Leningrad Electrical Engineering Institute of Communication, was founded. The success of all these institutions show how important technology was to the Soviets, particularly when it could be
used by the military.

My course load at LETI was heavy and included many theo-
retical and practical courses on radio communications and technology.
My instructors were enthusiastic about the new technology of radio
communications and we felt very privileged to be a part of this field.

By reading classical Russian novels, as well as foreign classics
translated into Russian, such as those by Stendahl, Dumas, Maupassant,
Jules Verne, and Jack London, I became very proficient in the language,
despite the fact I had not attended Russian elementary or secondary
schools and was never formally taught Russian.

Leningrad was a beautiful city, but I missed the warmth of Tiflis
and was frequently sick. Alexander Dumas wrote that he was "enchanted" by the white summer nights, when the sun hardly set, and by
the Neva River, which he called "pearl gray, iridescent as opal." However, Dumas was not in Leningrad (St. Petersburg, then) during the
winter, which lasted from October to May. The endless nights during
December, January, and February depressed me. Sometimes it was pitch
black for twenty full hours, with a heavy cloud cover obscuring the faint
sunshine for the other four hours. Lights were lit day and night and
smoke poured from chimneys, adding to the gloom.

Nevertheless, its golden spires and onion domes, the granite
columns and marble obelisks, were dazzling, summer and winter. (There
was little spring or fall.) Its architecture was more European than Russian and its culture and atmosphere a blend of Russia and the West.
One hundred and fifty arching bridges link the nineteen islands in the
Neva, and another four hundred bridges span its sixty canals. In his
poem, "The Bronze Horseman," Pushkin described a November flood
in Leningrad, "chill and without pity,"

Neva exploded, raging, yelling,
in kettle-like outbursts of steam—
until, mad as a beast, the stream
pounced on the city. . . .
Siege and assault! The waves, malicious,
like thieves, burst in through the windows. . . .
And all about is only water. . . .

In 1703 Peter the Great had built a fortress against the Swedes in this northernmost corner of Russia. This became (in succession) St. Petersburg, Petrograd, and Leningrad. Now it is St. Petersburg again. The town was built on a marsh with forced labor with considerable human sacrifice, some say tens of thousands perished during its construction. Yet it became an engineering masterpiece, comparable to Venice or Amsterdam. After Peter built his city, he forcibly moved his family and court here, 400 miles north of Moscow.

It was said that most of the artists, musicians, writers, and scientists lived in Leningrad, while the merchants, politicians, and bureaucrats preferred to live in Moscow, the seat of the central government. Leningrad was the headquarters of the prestigious Academy of Science, which had been founded in 1724 by Peter the Great, who encouraged scientific research for its own sake. The attitude toward science changed when the Academy came under control of the Soviet Council of Ministers in the late 1930s, after its move to Moscow. Then the emphasis was not exclusively on science, but also on the development of technology, particularly relating to defense. The criterion for being on the staff of the Academy moved from strict academic excellence to more of an emphasis on the depth of one's loyalty to the Communist Party.

The cultural life of Leningrad was exciting, with the Kirov Ballet, theaters, concerts, and operas. Its magnificent Hermitage Museum was the former Winter Palace of the tsars. I would wander through its halls, overwhelmed by its extravagance, awed by the crystal chandeliers, the enormous mirrors, the painted ceilings, Carrara marble staircases, and great paintings. I was always fond of ballet (and ballerinas) and I attended the Kirov Ballet Theater as often as I could, as well as performances at the various ballet studios. I seldom failed to buy flowers from my meager income to throw them to my favorite dancer in the night's production, but I never went backstage to meet one personally.

However, I had no time to enjoy Leningrad fully. Occasionally I was dragged to a girl's house, hoping, I suppose, to be passed on as a future husband. But I was not at all ready for marriage, and I closed my eyes to the soft light of summer nights when young couples held hands and walked alongside the Neva, whispering to each other. I was working hard on getting first a master's degree and then a degree of *kandidat nauk* (equivalent to a Ph.D.) in electrical (radio) communications. Nothing else mattered very much.

Well, one thing mattered: My continued infatuation with the United States of America. One summer while I was still a student I met an American girl in a park near the Institute. I immediately fell in love—not so much with her, as with the aura that surrounded her. Freedom! This would always be the great love of my life, and she represented that to me. Not only was she American, she was Armenian, as well. My passion was ignited! Ironically, she was infatuated with the Soviet Union and thought it much superior to the United States. After two days of bliss she left, giving me her pen as a souvenir. I in turn gave her a Russian ruble, with the thought that we would exchange our souvenirs when we met again. Although we promised each other faithfully that we would correspond, I never heard from her again, nor she from me.

Many years later, long after I had married and was living in America, I remembered and wondered what had become of her. Because I had forgotten her name and did not know her address, I put small classified ads in the Armenian-American newspapers: "Will the woman who was in Leningrad one summer and met a young engineering student please contact such and such?" A friend of hers saw the ad and told her about it.

She responded from Washington, D.C., and we made arrangements to meet at Grand Central Station in New York City. We were each to carry a newspaper as a way of identifying ourselves to the other. In that crush of thousands of travelers, I stood waiting while many trains came and went. Everyone, it seemed, was holding a newspaper. Certain that we could never find each other, I finally decided to leave. Just then I felt a tap on my shoulder and turned around. I was appalled! And I could not hide my disappointment. She was not the romantic figure I recalled, but a dumpy, homely, middle-aged woman, nothing resembling the girl I had known years earlier.

She asked me to take her home, which I agreed to do. In the taxi, she held my hand, whispering warmly, "I was always waiting for you! And I'm still here for you, after so many years."

We climbed the steps to my apartment, where my wife greeted us. "Your wife!" she cried. "I cannot believe you are married!" So, I was not the only one to be disappointed.

My wife graciously served us lunch, during which there was little conversation. Immediately afterward, my former girlfriend left. But before she did, she gave me a book which she had written in Armenian (published in the United States) about her long-ago trip to the Soviet Union and our meeting in Leningrad. When I finally brought myself to read it, I found it thoroughly ridiculous. For instance, she wrote that Russians didn't use locks on their doors because they were so honest! She thought all Soviet-made products were better than American-made ones, especially the automobiles—which were actually made in Detroit. And she thought it was "so cute" that I kept all my belongings, including my kitchen utensils, my linens, some books and stationery in the same closet.

I have a large, aquiline nose. This nose may be considered quite handsome among Armenians, but it was also a source of infection and pain for me in Leningrad. A peculiar condition caused the bones to grow together, making breathing through my nose very difficult when I was well and impossible when I had a cold, which was much of the time in that wintry climate. Eating was an arduous process, and talking while eating was out of the question. So I submitted to an operation that would chip away at the overgrowth of bone and allow my nasal passages to be open again. I had a very mild anesthetic for the operation, which seemed to last for decades. Afterward, the doctors could not stop the bleeding. They taped my nose shut, forcing the blood into my stomach, which became grossly distended. This torture continued for two weeks, when the bleeding finally stopped. The procedure helped somewhat and allowed me to survive the long winters.

I never joined the Communist Party, although I had several opportunities. Some of my friends did join, not out of political ideology, but to promote themselves in the Soviet hierarchy. That way they could get a better job, better housing, and other privileges, particularly goods, when there were shortages. Probably more of those in the intelligentsia (the *nauchnie rabotniki* or "brain workers") joined the party than those of the working class, for they could see the advantages of doing so. However, only a small percentage of the Soviet people were active Party members. Nonetheless, the influence of the Party was powerful.

Shortages were common in the Soviet Union in those years, even for the simplest items. I used to join a group of students who drank tea in a small cafe. Frequently we took turns using the one aluminum spoon to stir our drink. Before long, the spoon became fastened to the table with a steel wire so no one could walk off with it. One day when I tried to use this spoon to taste my tea, I discovered that it would not hold a drop—the center of the spoon had been drilled out to further discourage a thief!

Because I came from the Caucasus where life was relatively free, I had grown up without a sense of fear that characterizes so many Soviet people. Of course a school friend or two had betrayed me over the years and reported my bad behavior, but by and large we trusted each other. So it was a new and very uncomfortable sensation to realize that few of the people around me were trustworthy and many, in fact, were volunteer spies who were waiting for the moment to turn me in to the Soviet Secret Police.

I suppose my curiosity about how things worked and my love of freedom to explore new ideas marked me as a suspect. Therefore, I was always extremely careful not to express any anti-Soviet sentiment. I refused to say anything that might get me arrested, yet I always felt under surveillance and could never relax—like everyone else living in the Soviet Union.

Even before graduation, I carried out some electronic research in the Central Radio Laboratory of Leningrad, the hub of the best electronic brains. It had been established in 1923 as an applied science center, acting as a point of contact between industry and science. It was exciting for me, a novice, to be associated with the most prominent people in my field and to gain this valuable experience. While I was working there, I published two technical articles in Soviet periodicals describing some results of my work in radio communications.

Normally after graduation from a university, students were obliged to work for three years at any location the government told them to, whether they wanted to or not. This was a sort of repayment to the government for educating them. Some new graduates, especially Party members, would manage to avoid this compulsory assignment and would find a job in a large city. However, I was not one of them.

After graduation, I was sent to the Ural Mountains just northwest of Siberia to work on a secret defense project. After the first year, I was put in charge of a small scientific expedition to the Arctic region of the Soviet Union to investigate the propagation of short radio waves. The government felt it was crucial to map the Arctic region, and indeed in 1937 a famous Soviet pilot, V. P. Chkalov, flew over the Arctic to North America, proving that it could be done. During the 1930s the Defense Ministry was particularly interested in Finland, which had been a Russian duchy until it proclaimed its independence in 1917. The Soviets could see Finland's strategic advantage on the Baltic Sea and longed for it back.

Besides myself, our expedition consisted of a radio operator, a mechanic, and the driver. All our equipment was put in a covered six-axle flatbed truck. It had an oven in the center which kept us warm and which we used to cook our meals. Our entire route was mapped out in advance and we had to follow it closely, without any deviation. It was slow going on the primitive frozen roads, banked with snow. Visibility was frequently close to zero, either because of dense fog or blowing snow. And despite our fur parkas, oversized boots lined with grass, and four pairs of wool socks, we were never warm.

Every one hundred miles or so along the route we would take out our antennas to transmit radio signals by Morse code to a receiving station in the Urals. We did this to measure the strength of our signals as a function of the distance and the time of day. By the end of our journey we came very close to the northern border of Finland. I needed to send one more radio transmission from a particular site, which happened to be a few hundred feet on the Finnish side.

Since there was no border guard on that uninhabited snow-covered area, I ordered my driver to cross the border for a few minutes to make the necessary measurements. Instead, the driver suddenly drew his pistol! In a very menacing tone of voice he told me that if I insisted on crossing the border, he would arrest me. Then he showed me his credentials. He was my commissar, assigned to me by a Communist party official to keep me from escaping abroad—either accidentally or intentionally. From that point on, he took command of the expedition, and I became a suspect in his eyes.

After being relieved of my duties, I decided to leave the commissar and the truck and to race to Leningrad, hoping to get there before he did. I was sure he would press charges against me for "attempting to flee abroad." I had seen too many results of such charges and knew it would end not only my career, but also my freedom for many years.

In 1932 the NKVD, or state secret police, was given unusual power, the power to exile, deport, confine in labor camps, or execute anyone they judged guilty of treason, espionage, divulging military secrets, or fleeing abroad. Fleeing abroad, as I was alleged to have done, was punishable by death.

I remembered my former professor, Axelrod Berg, who by then was an admiral with a commanding position in the Admiralty. I had been a favorite student of his and hoped he could figure out something to save me from years in the prison or exile in Siberia. Once back in Leningrad, with trepidation I entered that imposing building with its great gilded spire and marble halls. I found him in an impressive office lined with maps and told him what had happened, asking for his help. He took pity on my desperate situation and decided that the best course of action would be to arrest me formally and put me to work on a "super important" defense project immediately in the Admiralty.

I agreed. As anticipated, within a few days the undercover commissar appeared at the Admiralty with two NKVD agents to arrest me. However, he was told that I was now working on a very important defense project and they couldn't touch me until it was over. In six months my admiral released me from the "project" and I was free. My case was closed. I was able to breathe again.

The scientific results of that expedition were published first in Soviet technical literature, and abstracted in the British magazine *Wireless Engineering* in February 1935. That was a great boost to my career. I was then working feverishly in my field and within a year published my first book, which was on automatic controls in radio receivers. It was the first book of its kind and was distributed widely. With the book came some prestige, but it didn't make my life easier.

Of all the shortages in the Soviet Union, perhaps the worst was the housing shortage. At that time I had secured a place to sleep, but not to live. It was not even a room, but simply space in the corridor of a seven-room apartment in a six-story building. This one apartment was occupied by seven different families, twenty-three inhabitants in all. There was one kitchen and one bathroom for all to share.

Late at night I would come "home" and roll out my mattress into the corridor. In the morning, before anyone was up, I would roll up my mattress, rush into the bathroom to clean up, and then go away until the next night. I lived this way for three or four months until I learned that a tenant, an old woman who lived alone in one of the rooms, had died.

The news spread all over the neighborhood with lightning speed. Within two days, her door was covered with more than two dozen padlocks put there by potential tenants in an attempt to keep others out. I was among them. So was a local militia officer. When the other candidates learned he was staking a claim, they immediately removed their padlocks, preferring not to compete with him. Finally there remained only two padlocks on the door. One was the officer's and the other was mine. I was desperate enough to take a chance.

This was a matter that had to be resolved by a local court. On the day it convened to decide who would get the room, the officer was so sure of himself that he didn't even bother to show up for the hearing. The judge, pretending not to notice his absence, asked me sarcastically, "Why do you think I should assign this room to you, rather than to the distinguished militia man and his family? He has the important duty of defending the security of our citizens against internal and external enemies of our glorious state!"

I knew that question was coming and I was prepared. I replied, "Of *course* you can assign the room to the militia man. However, have you thought what our beloved comrade Stalin would think of your action?"

"What do you mean!" he responded. "What has this room to do with our beloved comrade Stalin?"

"Ah," I continued, "if you have been reading the newspapers lately, you could not miss the articles describing how our beloved comrade Stalin spends sleepless night thinking how to improve the well-being of our young, talented engineers and scientists, the flower of our glorious society. Think of how much he wants to strengthen our industry—and then think about how he would regard your unwise, antisocial decision!"

As soon as I mentioned Stalin, the judge's self-assurance disappeared. The name had a magic effect.

"You don't have to tell me what our beloved comrade Stalin thinks," the judge said rather uncertainly. "I am a judge. I know better than you. The court will be in recess for fifteen minutes."

The fifteen minutes were not even up when the judge returned to the bench and resumed the hearing. Very tersely he said to me, "The room is yours."

I was delighted, but of course would not show it. I merely nodded and left the court, eager to move in to my "lavish" quarters with their promise of privacy. It was the first time I would have my own room. I was reminded of the story about a man who finally got a new apartment from the government after years of waiting. He was asked to praise the government publicly for this wonderful gift.

"I am so thankful to my government," he said, "for giving me this apartment. Now I can stand under my wonderful warm shower and forget my miserable life."

Later, when I accidentally ran into the militia man, he threatened "to fix me." He never expected that he would lose the room and was extremely angry. But he could do nothing. The decision had been made, thanks to Stalin's "help."

However, when I took the room I had no idea how much trouble it would be to share one kitchen and one bathroom with twenty-three others. Every morning there was a long queue at the bathroom door, and God forbid anyone had an emergency! No one would give way, and everyone had to wait his turn, no matter what. For such emergencies, we had chamber pots in our rooms.

Sharing a kitchen was just as difficult. We each had our own primus, or kerosene burner on which we cooked our meals. We couldn't stand in the kitchen for an hour or so watching while our soup cooked, but unless we *were* watching, our pots were likely to be "sabotaged." We learned that if we would be away from the kitchen, even briefly, we had to tie the lid on to the pot with steel wire to prevent our friendly *communards* from depositing dirt, insects, rodents, and even feces into it while it simmered. We became very hostile toward each other. On top of everything, there were a couple of informers who would report to the authorities any "suspicious" activities or anti-social talk. Each apartment house in Leningrad had its quota of these informers.

After I had been living in Leningrad for about eight years, I was given a few weeks off and took my first trip back to Tiflis. This time I had enough money for a "regular" railroad fare. The train had a twenty-minute stopover in Rostov-on-the-Don. As I was stretching my legs on the platform, I noticed a pretty girl standing there with her mother. I said "Hello" and she responded in a friendly way. We chatted for a few moments on unimportant matters.

I liked this slight, dark-haired girl at once—she seemed smart and strong-minded. When the train whistle sounded for me to get back on board, I was sorry. I told her that I'd be back in a month. Would she meet me at the station again? Yes, she would, she said with a smile and my heart began to sing. It sang all the way to Tiflis.

Seeing Tiflis again after so many years brought tears to my eyes. The funny wooden houses built into the hillsides were still there with their balconies crammed with people playing cards, drinking tea, and watching the street. My mother had mellowed somewhat, but still we were not close. All the time I was there, visiting friends and relatives, I was aware I no longer belonged. Tiflis was now for me just a vacation spot, not home.

I was not sad to leave, although I did not know when or if I'd ever return. My mind was on the young girl in Rostov-on-the-Don. Would she remember? I bought a large basket of grapes at our stopover at Ganzha to give to her. It was night as we approached Rostov and raining as well. My fellow passengers teased me that no girl in her right mind would be on the platform so late and in such weather. I was afraid they were right.

But she *was* there, her slight figure searching for me among the disembarking passengers.

"This is for you," I said when we met, handing her the basket of grapes. She took the heavy basket with both hands, giving me the chance to kiss her on the lips. Normally in those days, kissing a girl on the lips like that would get a slap on the face. In this case, her hands were occupied and the grapes were too beautiful to drop, so I was safe. In fact, she laughed and we exchanged addresses. After six months of correspondence, Virginia became my wife.

That episode proved a very well-known saying in Russia that no unmarried man can pass through the city of Rostov without being caught in romance and eventually marriage. Similarly, Odessa had a reputation for catching unmarried women. There the local boys stood on the platform, waiting to meet a potential bride. This is why Rostov was called "Rostov-Papa" and Odessa, "Odessa-Mama."

I learned a great deal from Virginia's letters. She was the only child of Arshak and Roza Megerian. Her father was a Social Democrat who was exiled to Rostov-on-the-Don by the Tsarist regime when he supported the 1905 uprising. Virginia was born in 1917, just before the Bolsheviks took over, and Arshak was jubilant about the two events. Unfortunately, he should have been less enthusiastic about the Bolsheviks. He had served his purpose in bringing the Bolsheviks to power and was no longer valuable to them. He was arrested and executed in 1921, when Virginia was only four years old. Her uncles and aunts also were arrested within that year and eventually died in exile.

Roza went to work in a fish factory to support herself and her daughter. Virginia's care was given over to a Russian-born German governess who taught her perfect *hoch Deutsch* (the "high" German of the educated class), a skill that would become very important to our survival in later years. Now, in 1934, Virginia was a quiet, somewhat introverted seventeen years old. She made plans to visit an uncle in Leningrad and I could hardly wait to see her again.

On a cold, wintry day I met her at the Leningrad railroad station. What a surprise! This was not the lovely young girl I had become enchanted with six months earlier. She looked emaciated, her face was flushed and she was shivering under her heavy coat. Clearly, she was very ill. The uncle, who was supposed to meet her to take her to his home did not show up. This was rather strange, because he was the one who had invited her to visit! I felt I had no choice; I took her home with me.

I did not plan to keep her at my place. I knew she needed medical care, and suspected that she had tuberculosis, which was rampant then. I tried at once to get her into a hospital, but she was refused admittance because she was not a Leningrad resident. The Soviet government had established the system of issuing internal passports. Everyone had to have "papers." Virginia's papers had been issued in Rostov.

She was a stranger in Leningrad and entitled to nothing.

So, unwillingly, I became both her doctor and her nurse. In my small, airless room she gradually recovered to the point of being able to take care of herself, but she remained frail for years. She was a good patient and did not complain unreasonably, I thought. At the end of the ordeal, I still felt quite warmly toward her and she toward me, for we got married as soon as she felt up to it.

It was not long before the tenants in our building extended to her the same animosity they showed to me. She, too, learned quickly to trust no one and to think with a craftiness that would keep us out of the Gulag. For instance, practically all the telephones in the building were bugged with a microphone that could pick up conversations in the room. Virginia made a soundproof pillow to cover our telephone so that we could speak to each other without being overheard. This made our room especially popular with our friends. As soon as anyone entered, Virginia would gesture to them not to open their mouths until she covered the telephone.

Life was very difficult in the early 1930s in Soviet Russia, as Stalin's paranoia and craving for power became more apparent. We felt in constant danger from the secret police. Yet we couldn't help making fun of our situation and would whisper jokes to those we trusted. Laughter was a life-saver and—provided we didn't get arrested for it—was as good for our health as any vitamin. (There was a shortage of vitamins anyway.)

When asked, "How are you?" a Soviet citizen typically answered, "Better than tomorrow."

A favorite story was about an old woman who ran to catch a packed city bus. "Thank God!" she gasped when she got on board.

A citizen immediately corrected her. "You know there is no God. You should say, 'Thank Stalin!'"

"You're right," she agreed. "But what should I say if Stalin dies one day?"

"In that case," he replied, "perhaps you should say 'thank God!'"

Another story told how one militia man asked another what he thought about Stalin. "The same thing that you are thinking," he answered.

"Never mind what *I* think. What do *you* think?" the first militia man persisted.

The second militia man repeated, "The same thing you think."

"In that case," said the first militia man, "I have to arrest you."

One of my favorites concerns an Armenian who was asked, "What would happen to the Sahara Desert if the Soviet government got hold of it?"

He answered, "Nothing in particular the first year, or even the second year, but in the third year, there would be an acute shortage of sand!"

The head of the Communist Party in Leningrad at this time was Sergei Kirov, a dynamic and popular Russian who was considered Stalin's greatest comrade-in-arms. Despite his popularity, he had at least four bodyguards whenever he moved around the city—and he loved to walk the streets each day, starting with a stop at a barber shop. On December 1, 1934, on his way to a meeting of city commissioners in a government building, he was shot point blank.

The assassin, who was caught immediately, was said to be Leonid Nikolaev, a thirty-year-old unemployed "social misfit." No one doubted that Nikolaev pulled the trigger, but many questions were raised—privately, in whispers. Where were Kirov's bodyguards? How did an armed man get into a building so closely watched by the NKVD? How did Nikolaev's wife get the 50,000 rubles found in their apartment? And, despite Stalin's great show of grief, wasn't it convenient that his strongest rival was now gone? For Kirov was a moderate who opposed terrorist activity.

This was the beginning of Stalin's Great Terror, conducted by his henchman, Nikolai Yezhov, head of the secret police. Among those "tried" and executed were trusted comrades of Stalin—Zinoviev, Kamenev, and Rykov, who were charged with counterrevolutionary conspiracy. All intellectuals became suspect and in our installation, many mature and seasoned scientists were arrested, accused of treason, and shot or sent into permanent exile. The purge was devastating to the development of Soviet science throughout the country.

Virginia and I had been married about a year at that time, and I was transferred to a research institute deep in the woods outside of Leningrad. Our work was top secret and because it was considered necessary to the defense of the country, our working conditions were superior to those in the city. By Soviet standards, our housing and food were more than adequate. When Virginia joined me in the country her health continued to improve, thanks to the fresh air and plentiful food. We were expecting a baby by then and she needed the extra nourishment.

But we could not escape Stalin's Terror and finally it reached our lab also. The younger scientists, like myself, were spared arrest and exile. Instead, we were evicted from the laboratory in the middle of the night and brought back to Leningrad. There we were put under house arrest for fourteen months without the right to work anywhere. We were given a so-called Wolf's ID, which meant that no other institution was permitted to hire us in any capacity. We were allowed to leave our homes only for short walks, and I could feel our small room get smaller. Virginia's gift for silence was particularly appreciated during this time. Everyone in the building was frightened and we all started speaking in whispers.

At this time, when I had no source of income, our son Karik was born. Virginia and I had to sell practically all our belongings just to sustain our lives. We still lived in the same six-story building, which was occupied chiefly by intellectuals. There were "too many thinking people" for the government's comfort and so we were under constant surveillance by the NKVD. Every city and town had its "quota" of how many people should be liquidated in that area to make it safe for Stalin. Too many would affect industry; too few was perceived as a threat to Stalin's power. Leningrad had a higher "quota" than many cities because of the large number of intellectuals there.

Knowing this, the population kept a very low profile and avoided expressing strong opinions on any subject. The following joke explains that point of view:

A sparrow falls down in the snow, numb from cold. A cow passes by and s**ts on top of the sparrow. It warms up the sparrow, who sticks out its head and chirps. An eagle flies over, grabs the sparrow and kills it.

The moral: Not everyone who puts you in s**t is your enemy. Not everyone who takes you out of s**t is your friend. Therefore, when you are in s**t up to your neck, do not chirp!

My friend Sacha was an electrical engineer who was sent to Yerevan, the capital of the Soviet Armenian Republic, to conduct the final inspection of a newly completed radio station. During the inspection, while testing the electric knife switches, the blade of one of the switches broke in his hand. Noting the poor workmanship, Sacha said angrily, "How could such junk be manufactured by our industries?"

That was enough. Two days later he was arrested for anti-Soviet remarks, specifically for "criticizing the Soviet industry." He was put in jail and became a non-person. When his wife had not heard from him after many years, she presumed him dead and remarried. Their two children were adopted by their stepfather.

Many more years went by. Then one winter morning I received a telephone call from a man speaking good (literary) Armenian. He asked if I could spare time to see him. When he walked into my room, I could hardly believe my eyes. It was my good friend Sacha, just released from jail!

I was especially amazed to hear him speak Armenian instead of Russian. He explained that in Armenia he had shared his prison cell with a leading Armenian poet who taught him to speak beautiful Armenian. I asked him if he was bitter for wasting so many years of his life in prison and losing his family.

His answer surprised me. "Not at all," he said. "Perhaps it was necessary for our government to do this to me."

This was a typical Slavic attitude which enabled millions of people who were prosecuted and condemned for no good reason to tolerate the terrible injustice of life in the Soviet Union. With such a mentality, the government could "get away with murder" and it did, thousands of times.

A large blackboard hung in the lobby of our apartment build-ing, as in many other communal buildings in Soviet republics, with names of the most "undisciplined" tenants listed—those most likely to create a nuisance or vandalize the place. Strangely enough, these people were safe from arrest, because in the eyes of the government, they were the least dangerous to Soviet security. Knowing this, Virginia tried to create the impression that we were a nuisance to others. Our name became a permanent fixture on the boards and we were never arrested by the secret police, whereas a majority of our building tenants were arrested and deported to the Gulag.

Still, the government had to be sure we were not subversives. I was looking for an *au pair* at that time to help Virginia with the baby. She was still very weak. Apparently the NKVD got wind of my search and sent us an attractive blonde country girl. She lived in the room with us, rolling out her mattress on the floor between my and my wife's beds—a very cozy arrangement. No wonder that we had only one child!

She was a good worker and we did not suspect her true identity until one day I came across her notes by accident. She was making weekly reports to the police about our guests—and, of course, about their conversations. This discovery, which we kept from her, had a chill-ing effect on us. We realized then how dedicated the police were to catching us in an anti-Soviet act. But what could we do about it? We could not fire her. That would cause an immediate reprisal. Yet, how could we continue to live with her in our midst and perhaps compro-mise our friends?

Finally I thought of a solution. I found a young man who had just been discharged from the army and who was looking for a bride. I introduced him to our domestic and—lo and behold!—one day the girl told us with tears in her eyes that she had to leave because she was going to marry this man. We too wept crocodile tears and told her how we'd miss her. As soon as we closed the door behind her, we sighed with enormous relief.

However, our building superintendent was still suspicious. To have better access to our conversations and visitors, he managed to evict our next-door neighbor and occupy the room himself. Then he installed primitive listening devices on our adjacent wall. It did not take long for me to detect them. Our defense was to bang on our common wall, to his great annoyance. But he couldn't do anything about it—after all, thanks to his blackboard, everyone knew we were nuisances.

Being "anti-social" was sometimes very gratifying. One woman in the apartment was especially nasty to my little son. I decided to retaliate. Once when she was alone in the kitchen, I pushed her head into the sink full of dirty water, keeping it there until she promised not to harm my son again. She promised at once and kept that promise.

Our building was in a U-shape with a larger inner courtyard. Our window faced the windows of other tenants on the opposite side of the courtyard. This arrangement made me an unwilling witness to midnight raids, when NKVD agents would enter tenants' apartments and forcefully evict the men, leaving behind hysterical women and children. These scenes of horror were unfolding in front of our eyes every night. No one was safe and everyone in the building expected to be next.

I was also waiting my turn and was prepared for that paralyzing knock on the door. Yet days passed and there was still no knock. By then I was one of the few men left. Then one night, it was New Year's Eve, we heard the knock. It was too much for Virginia. She collapsed on the floor. My one-year-old son was awakened and started to cry. I put on my coat, kissed my family, knowing there was little chance of my seeing them again, and opened the door.

Standing there was our superintendent in the company of a man in uniform. I said, "I am ready. Let's go. Just don't hurt my wife and child."

The uniformed man gave me a paper and requested me to sign. I thought it was probably the standard Soviet procedure, admitting that I was being arrested for my "counter-revolutionary activities." I signed it. Did I have any choice?

But instead of dragging me out, the uniformed man handed me a copy of the paper I had just signed. Then he left with the superintendent, leaving me behind. With trembling hands I tried to read what was written on the paper. It was a telegram from a friend in Moscow, wishing me a happy new year!

The Yezhov terror against intellectuals reached its peak in 1938. Then, Yezhov, the chief of the Secret Police responsible for the unprecedented terror which swept the entire country and which took the lives of millions of innocent people, himself became a victim of the terror and was executed. The even more notorious Lavrenti Beria took his place. Those of us persecuted by Yezhov who were still alive were told that the persecutions were an "error in judgment" and we were permitted to "rehabilitate" ourselves through a mock court procedure.

I don't know what happened to others in a similar position, but I was "rehabilitated" under the condition that I not seek work in any defense establishment. I had no choice but to switch to teaching, first at the Industrial Academy of Leningrad and later, when that institution dissolved, at the Leningrad Institute of Electrical Engineering, my alma mater.

At this time it required "special clearance" to look at a cover of the American magazine *Popular Mechanic* that carried a photograph of an early radar device. The Soviet government was deeply suspicious of anything American, yet the two countries had the same interest in technology. Several electronic scientists were sent periodically to RCA Corporation for a six-month training program at their laboratories in New Jersey. Although I was never chosen to go, many of my colleagues and subordinates were. (I learned later that Soviet officials thought that if I were ever allowed out of the country, I would never come back. True.) When these highly educated men returned, they were given three months to write a detailed report of what they had learned. Then, inexplicably, some of them were assigned to outposts in Siberia. I asked no questions, but I wondered what they had done to deserve such treatment.

Many Soviet scientists were then interested in the development of television. A Russian-born American scientist, Vladimir T. Zworykin, was generally credited with inventing the iconoscope, which made the electronic transmission of images possible. Zworykin had been educated in Leningrad before emigrating to the United States in 1919. In the late 1930s, he made a short visit to Leningrad, bringing a prototype of one of these electronic television sets with him.

After his visit, Zworykin left the television set with his sister in Leningrad. There was one experimental television station then, and a few television sets had been installed in homes of high-ranking party officials and at public clubs. We heard later that after he'd been gone only a little while, engineers, obviously directed by the NKVD, arrived at his sister's door, asking to borrow the set for a few days. They took it completely apart, looking for who-knows-what, and then they found that they were unable to put it back together. So much for the exchange of technological information!

In the fall of 1939 the Soviet Union requested of Finland that it be allowed to construct a naval base on the Karelian Isthmus. Finland refused. Claiming that Finland (population two million) had attacked her (population more than two hundred million) the Soviet Union declared war on that Baltic nation and sent in hundreds of thousands of troops. The Finns fought back fiercely. During that Winter War the entire free world was hypnotized by the drama in this little democratic nation.

To keep us up-to-date on their version of this war, the Soviet government used radio and a public address system. Speakers were installed in all public buildings and most apartment houses. Frequent bellicose announcements kept those of us in Leningrad, so close to the border, in a state of tension and fear. Food was rationed for a while, especially butter and sugar, and there were long lines at all the food shops.

The Russo-Finnish War was conducted so badly by the Soviets, and the Finnish resistance was so fierce, that the entire operation cost the Soviets tens of thousands of casualties. To keep their casualties secret, the Soviet government sent injured soldiers to hospitals far away from Leningrad. Damaged tanks were hidden in junkyards outside the city protected by six-foot high wooden fences.

The Finn's hatred of the Russian Soviets was total. Soldiers defending their positions against approaching Soviets would chain themselves to the tops of trees, so that if they were hit, they would not fall and could continue to fire their weapons. Finnish children carried grenades hidden under their clothing, throwing them at Soviet soldiers, often at the cost of their own lives. Finnish families evacuated from their homes often poisoned the food left in the house, hoping to kill a few more soldiers. And wounded Finnish soldiers taken to Soviet hospitals would refuse food, preferring to starve to death than eat from the hand of their enemy.

Not being able to crush little Finland, the Soviets were forced to sign a peace treaty with her on March 12, 1940. The treaty gave the Soviet Union several strategic border territories and a buffer zone from Germany. A Soviet naval base was finally built on Hanko Peninsula.

The limited conditions of the treaty was greeted with bitterness by many, especially by the wounded soldiers and by the families of the deceased. "Is this what we were fighting for and paying for with the blood of tens of thousands of lives?" they asked each other. Much later we learned that a secret agreement between Stalin and Hitler allowed the Soviets to occupy Finland.

By then World War II was already raging in Europe. Poland had been divided between Germany and the Soviet Union and there was an open declaration of friendship between Hitler and Stalin, which, we were told, would save the Soviet Union from active participation in the war. This seemed incredible to us, after years of hearing anti-German propaganda.

This was to be a "new era." People with Jewish names were quietly removed from their positions. The jamming of German broadcasting stopped. The radio industry started receiving all types of modern equipment, instruments, and technical literature from Germany. German authors and composers suddenly became popular. It was a remarkable overnight change, and we were more than a little leery.

Now we heard that France, Britain, and the United States were "warmongers." I even heard that Hitler's photograph appeared in some Soviet homes. In the meantime, Poles in Soviet-occupied territories were being deported to the Gulag by the tens of thousands. Moreover, four thousand elite Polish military personnel captured by the Soviets in the spring of 1940 were executed in Katyn Forest outside Smolensk and their bodies dumped in a mass grave. (This was discovered three years after the fact by German soldiers and many years later finally acknowledged by the Soviet government.)

For now, the Soviet population in general was bewildered about what was happening, not knowing if we would be involved in the war. I was extremely busy with my work and was spending about sixteen hours a day at the Institute, teaching and conducting research work. I was making enough money to take care of my family and buy a few extras. One "extra" was a vacation each year for Virginia. She was still not healthy and needed time to recuperate. In mid-June 1941, I put Virginia and Karik on the train for Anapa, a health resort on the Black Sea, where they could live in a boarding house for a few weeks. As a parting gift, I presented them with forty pounds of sugar, which I had gathered painstakingly over the weeks. This would serve them better than money. In a week I would join them myself for a well-earned rest.

Or that was what I thought I would do until Sunday, June 22, 1941. In the early hours of that day, the German Army unexpectedly attacked the Soviet Union.

General view of Old Tiflis (now Tibilisi) the capital of the Georgian Republic. The statue is of the founder of the city, King Vaktang Gorgansali.

This is the way my Mother was negociating with the yogurt vendor. (Elibekian)

A kiosk with theatrical announcements in 3 languages: Georgian, Armenian and Russian. Note the play Macbeth by Shakespeare, on the right (in Russian). (Elibekian)

I, at age 3, with my Mother, in Tiflis.

My dapper Father at the time he met my Mother.

Left–Balcony of the apartment in the house where I spent my early years. On the right is the house where the Russian poet M. Lermontov lived during his exile from St. Petersburg, Russia, in the 1800's.

My family in Tiflis. Mother is on the left, Father is on the right, Brother on top.

Leningrad (now St. Petersburg), from a postcard.

Admiral Axel Ivanovitch Berg, my favorite professor (LETI).

THREE

*T*hat Sunday morning I snapped on my radio to pick up a broadcast symphony from one of the no-longer proscribed German stations. But instead of Beethoven or Brahms, I heard an announcement which gave me the shock of my life: The German army, by order of the Fuehrer, was advancing across the Soviet border at many points "to crush Communism and liberate the people."

Quickly I switched off my set, fearful that this tremendous knowledge would somehow implicate me. Perhaps some of the other people in the house knew about this, I thought, and wandered out into the hall. But my neighbors acted as if they were totally oblivious of the news. Returning to my room, I switched on the set again, tuning in a Leningrad station. I heard the ominous ticking of a metronome, interrupted every few minutes by a voice saying; "Attention! There will be an important announcement at 11 o'clock." I knew what that meant: During the Finnish war all important announcements, good and bad, were introduced that way.

My neighbors began crowding into my room, alerted by the sound of the excellent radio I had built. I felt surrounded. Four of them were Communist Party members and three of these were suspected "domestic spies." In such "cozy" company, I tried to look impassive, not yet knowing what the "official announcement" would be. But as Molotov's words began to fill my small room, it was difficult for any of us to hide our shock. He was then prime minister of the U.S.S.R.

"The Germans," he said, "in violation of all their promises have crossed the Soviet Union border and are moving forward. The Red Army has been ordered to throw back the enemy. You are to remain calm. You are to remain at work. Do not rush to the stores to purchase supplies. Do not hoard."

We reacted in typical Soviet fashion and rushed to the nearest stores. I bought the biggest slab of bacon I could find. Like the great mass of non-political people of the Soviet Union, we gave no thought to the ideological consequences of the German invasion. No one spoke of "the defense of the Soviet fatherland." That was to come later, and only from the government's propaganda broadcasts. We were interested in the immediate, day-to-day problems of eating and sleeping, of keeping warm.

After taking my first steps in self-preservation, I wracked my brain trying to think of what else I could do. The next day I joined the crowds assaulting the post offices, wanting to cash their government bonds. Cashiers were working steadily, handing out rubles to panicky people who were convinced that it was now or never. Those who had bank accounts were drawing out every kopeck. With all the money I could get together, I ran to one of the few people in Leningrad I trusted. Clara Holmquist was a Russian-born Swede and an old friend whose husband had been sent to Siberia. She was very practical and would be able to tell me how best to spend this money.

"Buy food," said Clara. "Food that will last for a long time. All the food you can lay your hands on. Sugar is very important. Salami is good, too."

So I went out to the shops again, making purchases here and there, being careful not to attract attention. Then I returned to my room to store what I had bought.

Also on Monday, June 22, I wired my wife in Anapa. I told her not to return to Leningrad, no matter what news she heard. I knew that her first impulse would be to do so at once. But it took no student of geography to realize that Leningrad would be threatened very soon by the German advance. My instructions to Virginia were very specific: She was to stay there until I was permitted to leave Leningrad. She was not to endanger herself or Karik. She was not to worry unduly if she did not hear from me.

It was very difficult for me to insist that Virginia remain away. I needed her more than ever before. And though I knew that many wives were on their way back, I also knew that they were inviting death. I don't know how I was so sure of this; none of us dreamed that the siege of Leningrad would be the horror it was. Perhaps it was some sixth sense, or that sensitivity to danger which people who live in a police state develop.

Urged on, ironically, by government announcements that there was plenty of food, we flocked to the food shops, where we found that the clerks had been ordered to let us buy as much as we wanted in order to quiet us down. If Moscow had gone to such lengths to convince us all was well, things were truly grave.

The next day, I got proof that my insight had been correct. A *ukase* or government decree was broadcast forbidding any resident to possess more than a two-day ration of food. Anyone discovered with food in excess of this would be severely punished. But although every instinct warned me that hoarding might mean punishment, I knew that *not* hoarding could mean death.

I continued to buy whatever I could, where and when I could— bread, sugar, vegetable oil, salt, canned foods, whatever I could find. When I had packed the space behind the large wall speaker in my room, I tore apart my books and put food between the bindings. I was determined not to be caught short. This obsession was somewhat illogical. Any day I could be drafted and my entire accumulation would be seized by my neighbors the moment I left. I think I continued buying because in those jittery days it gave me something to do and prevented my sitting around brooding on the future.

Tension was apparent everywhere. Among my intimate friends, those who were not afraid to discuss politics with me, this took the form of lengthy analyses of the situation. For a long time they had realized that only some outside force could crumple the Soviet dictatorship, and they had hoped that this would be one of the western democracies. Now they saw this liberation coming from Germany, a nation they abhorred and mistrusted. The older people, whose memories went back to World War I, remembered how Germans had treated Russians then and warned those who were falling under the spell of persuasive Nazi propaganda that to believe one totalitarian state was just as dangerous as to believe another.

Late in the afternoon of the war's third day, the Red Army issued a communiqué claiming that it had thrown the Germans back. But when we looked at the map, it was obvious that the fighting was moving steadily east. I had learned that the Germans now occupied the Ukraine. There they had commandeered all the produce of that rich agricultural region. It was as if the door to the nation's pantry had suddenly slammed shut.

North of Leningrad, Finns, still filled with hatred for Soviet Russians, had joined the German forces there. We were becoming encircled by the enemy. There would be no way out of the city except by airplane or by boat across Lake Ladoga to the east. Both routes were closed to the average citizen. We would be forced to sit and wait for rescue. If this was a shock, it was quickly superseded by another: Our daily slogans had suddenly changed. It was no longer, "For Stalin," but, "For the Fatherland, for Honor, and for Freedom." This, we were sure, meant that the war was going badly. Shortly afterward, we were ordered to turn in our radios. The government's reason was obvious: There was too wide a discrepancy between Soviet and German broadcasts.

Now we were dependent for our news solely on the government public address system. Speakers were in almost every apartment building and in all public places. As long as we got only the "official news," we would remain ignorant of the course of battle. But I was determined to keep informed.

I decided on a risky course of action. I had built two sets. I turned in one of these and dismantled the other, hiding the parts about my room. I knew I could put the set together hastily when I needed to. Besides, there had been no order to turn in radio *parts*.

Early in July, the public address system blared out that all children were to be taken out of the city to places of refuge. Parents were given two days to make preparations. On the appointed day, after tearful farewells, thousands of children were packed into trains. But before long, we learned that the children were moving in the direct line of the German advance through Pskov and Luga, instead of going east—typical Soviet planning. Desperate mothers left Leningrad without passes and against orders to rescue their children. Some were successful, but others found that their children had already been captured. These mothers, half-crazed with fear and grief, returned to Leningrad, and for the first time in my life I heard the government bitterly and openly denounced without reprisal by the NKVD.

In July, the government began organizing us into civilian guards. Every office had regular drill periods, although no one was given a real rifle. Even at the risk of having badly trained soldiers, the government did not trust the people with arms, so fearful was it of revolution. On the same day that we began this mock training we were warned that anyone who spread rumors would be shot immediately. But there was no need to make up stories. The news grew bleaker every day. We were all sure it was a question of days before the Soviet Union would collapse. Vitebsk, Pskov, and Smolensk had already fallen to the victorious Germans.

Then the air attack began. One day we had seventeen air raid alarms and three air battles. The battles were really a farce. The German Luftwaffe would circle the city, drop its bombs and fly off. Only then would the Soviet fighters take to the sky, go through a few motions, and then return to their base. After such a "battle," indignant recitals could be heard all over the city—after the sacrifices we had made to build a strong army and air force, this was the result!

The removal of all private telephones at this time did not raise public morale. We were never given any reason for this move, nor were we told why all telephone directories were destroyed simultaneously. But we realized that behind the action was that terrible fear of an uprising which, more than a fear of the Germans, seemed to be motivating all governmental directives.

When war had broken out, Molotov had promised us solemnly that there would never be food rationing, that enough had been stored away in strategic spots to last Leningrad for years. A month after the fighting started, our food purchases were limited drastically. For me, it was not too bad. I had been called back to the Institute and could make use of its cafeteria where, for one ruble, I could buy a small lunch.

Then the order came that we were to dig trenches on the Leningrad periphery. My name appeared on the work detail. This digging was to be done at night, and the next day we were expected to carry out our regular duties. That evening thousands of us gathered for a night of hell. We worked out in the open, with no place to hide when the Luftwaffe began strafing. Our own fighters had vanished and we had no protection. From 8:30 p.m. until dawn we alternately shoveled and frantically threw ourselves on the ground, trying to escape German bombs.

On several occasions the German planes showered leaflets instead of bombs. The penalties for picking up this propaganda were severe. However, like many people, I was able to stuff a leaflet into my pocket. The next morning in the privacy of my room, I read it in a state of astonishment and shock. These were the first anti-Soviet words I had ever seen in black and white. As I read, I kept looking over my shoulder, expecting an NKVD man to materialize suddenly and seize me. Over and over, I studied the leaflet, although it was stupidly worded and showed that the writer—probably a Tsarist émigré—had little understanding of the situation here. But still I wanted to keep that piece of paper. It was my one hold on a world where criticism of the all-powerful government in Moscow did not mean death or Siberia.

As July moved into August, many of the important Party leaders began to disappear from Leningrad. At the same time, some military schools in the city began to get evacuation orders.

"What is to become of us?" we asked one another. That became the theme song of the entire city in those days. Although we did not believe that the Germans had any intention of liberating us, we all agreed that nothing could be worse than life under the Soviets. The

Leningradskaya Pravda, official daily of the Communist Party and the largest newspaper in the city, was full of German atrocity stories. We did not believe them, so low was the prestige of the Soviet press. The only way I could get any factual information was by listening to Finnish broadcasts on my illegal set. Unlike the Germans, the Finns reported on what was actually going on, on how the opposing armies were making out. There was none of the heavy abuse characteristic of German broadcasts. Now and then the Finns would prod us a little by asking quietly, "What does equality of the sexes mean in Russia? Equality to do heavy labor? What do your children get to make up for the pleasures of childhood which they had lost? Rations?"

From Soviet sources all we got were reports of the glorious deeds of our retreating soldiers. When this did not bolster our morale, the theaters and the ballet, which had closed when war broke out, were reopened.

The evacuation of Leningrad continued haphazardly, without order or system. Scientific supplies and equipment, scientists who might be of use to the Germans, engineers, and works of art were sent away. Two electric power plants were dismantled and shipped out, but the important parts were left behind and wrecked to keep the Germans from using them. Those who wanted to stay were ordered to leave. Those who were desperate to leave began to clamor that they wanted to stay. I merely sat tight, expecting that I would be mobilized at any moment.

On August 7 the government mounted an exhibition of captured German trophies—a Junkers U-88, a Messerschmitt 109, a few German tanks—but we were not permitted to get too close to them. These, too, were "military secrets." Young people stared at the planes. One student said in a low voice, "Look, the Germans have planes too." Then he added ironically, "I thought *we* had all the planes." This spirit of irony also came out when we heard announcements of great air raids by Soviet planes on Berlin. No one had to tell us that we didn't even have control of the air over Leningrad.

Early in August I received a letter from my wife. It was unhappy, panicky. She reported that all the people she knew had fled Anapa. She was afraid to stay there alone. She did not have any money left. Could she return to Leningrad? I immediately ran out of the house with a few valuable books which I knew I could sell. With the money I received for them and with what other money I could borrow, I scraped together 600 rubles which I sent to her, forbidding her to come under any circumstances whatsoever.

Day after day, as the Germans advanced toward Leningrad, the news from the government continued to be optimistic: The Germans were far away and the Red Army had engaged them successfully. Therefore it was a terrific shock when the first long-range artillery shells smashed into the city and hit a four-story building near the October Station, killing seven people. Crowds from all parts of the city gathered to see this evidence of the proximity of the Germans. Police and firemen worked feverishly to cover the huge hole with tarpaulins, as if to hide it from the population. For a while, the government continued trying to hide the damage done by heavy shells, but we all knew what was happening. "How could the Red Army permit the Germans to get so close?" was a frequently uttered question and usually came from a bewildered Party member who had been lulled by rosy reports.

At last, two months after the Germans had violated Soviet territory, Voroshilov, the minister of defense, and Zhdanov, the Party chief of Leningrad were forced to admit that the enemy was at our gates. Considerably more serious was the news that the Leningrad-Murmansk and Leningrad-Moscow roads had been cut and all evacuation had ceased. Thousands of crates of technical equipment littered the streets near the railway stations. In offices and various scientific institutes stood mountains of other crates

Those of us who remained in the beleaguered city were now told that we would have to devote our free time to training in street warfare. We at the Institute were required to report in the courtyard each morning for instruction in throwing Molotov cocktails, attacking tanks, and so forth. But we were still not given any rifles. Such a step was considered too risky by the authorities. It was a sad sight to see white-haired professors, men with little strength left in them, being made to "train," although they were short of breath, rheumatic, or just too old. In charge of this drill was our political commissar, a man who could barely read or write.

"Get going," he would snap at an old professor of world renown. "You spent enough years polishing the seat of your chair. It's about time you did something for your fatherland. Get moving." And he would brandish his pistols. Because he was not very intelligent, he came to the conclusion that if he were particularly brutal to Jews, he would be spared by the Germans when they took over. This was a belief shared by many others of the Party elite. It was curious to see how easily the Communists could become anti-Semites. The same thing happened in the Caucasus as the Germans approached.

These pathetic defense measures were accompanied by more serious preparations. The government was getting ready to abandon Leningrad. Day and night, government employees burned official papers. All district Party committees destroyed their documents. Even house managers, the people who kept records of each person, his activities and friends, were told to destroy their records. No trace of the identities of Party members would be left for Germans to single out.

Toward the end of August, we were being bombed by the Germans every night. Their planes were met with plenty of anti-aircraft fire, but, despite wild claims, none was ever shot down. Ships of the Baltic fleet were moved into the center of the city, on the Neva River, but no one knew why, since no one knew whether or not Leningrad would become a battlefield or an open city. By the beginning of September, no one cared. Food supplies were very low and famine was more than a threat. Unlike the British, who during the German blitz distributed food among the London population, the Soviets hoarded their food reserves in a giant depot in the city. During the first major bombing of Leningrad, on September 8, the depot was completely destroyed—another example of the criminal stupidity of the "centralized Soviet planning" mentality.

Food—that was the main topic of our conversation and concern. In September the Soviet government issued ration cards for all types of food, whether bought in a store or restaurant. Laborers were allowed 400 grams (14 ounces) of bread a day; white-collar workers were entitled to 300 grams; dependents of workers were tossed a 200-gram bread ration. In October, this was cut in half and the bread itself seemed to be made of anything but flour. (We learned later it was made primarily of sawdust.)

From the start of the war, even when food was relatively plentiful I began a practice which I believe saved my life. With rigid discipline, despite my gnawing hunger, I divided my daily bread ration in two and put aside one of the halves_first drying it out. These hard crusts of bread continued to accumulate, and in the days when we had nothing, I still had a few crumbs to keep body and soul together.

One night—it was the 19th of September—my turn came up for air raid warden duty on the roof of my building. That night, the Kirovsk plant in the Petrograd section of the city was hit by fire bombs. It was a beautiful and terrible sight to see Leningrad silhouetted against a flickering red backdrop. Before this theatrical splendor, I forgot that German planes were circling overhead. I stood at the roof edge and watched in awe as part of my beloved city burned.

Soon afterward I ran into an acquaintance named Lala, who lived in the next building. She was the wife of an NKVD official, and my conversations with her had always been highly circumspect and "patriotic," because I knew that every word I said made its way to the NKVD. This time I put on the usual act about the villainous attack on the happiest and most free country in the world. But Lala would have none of it and interrupted nervously to tell me that her husband had just been called to the front. Before going he had warned her that the Germans would be in Leningrad the next day.

She wanted me to stay at her apartment for the next few days so that she would not be alone when the Germans occupied the city. I could see no reason for refusing. Unlike what most of us knew as home, her apartment was a beautiful and luxurious place. There were heavy oriental rugs on the floor and modern mahogany furniture. Lala set the table with old sterling silver, crystal, and fine china. There was wine on the table—a Spanish champagne. I could see that the NKVD lived well.

That evening, for the first time in many weeks, I ate a hearty meal. And after the first glass of wine, Lala suddenly confessed that she was the daughter of a Tsarist colonel and that she married her NKVD husband only for the comfort and safety he could offer her. To prove it, she brought out some old papers for me to see. But she was not revealing anything the NKVD didn't already know. As a matter of fact, it was considered fashionable among the high Soviet officials to marry women with Tsarist backgrounds.

Lala was sure that her husband would not return. She asked me if the document proving that she came from a Tsarist family would help her with the Germans. How could I give her an answer? I had only her word for it that she was not leading me on. In the Soviet Union it took only one mistake, one error in judgment about a person's sincerity, to finish you off. So I made only a few noncommittal remarks. The next day, when the Germans had not arrived, Lala began worrying about what she had told me. I stayed another day and then left.

Toward the end of September, I had two visitors: My neighbor Sittin, a Communist Party member and fellow engineer, and Lev, an old schoolmate. Sittin came late at night and after an uncomfortable silence, blurted out, "I want you to know that I was never really a Communist. If I spied on you, I was pressed to do it. But I never reported on you—that's why you are still free today. Let's be friends."

For years he had been my tormentor and now he was asking me to forget it! I wanted to throw him out. But there was no way of knowing whether he was sincere or was trying to provoke me to attack the regime. It was an old trick among Communists to take the part of the disillusioned in order to trap a victim. So, instead of giving myself the luxury of beating him up, I answered seriously: "It is every man's duty to be true to the ideals of Lenin and Stalin and to die for them if necessary." Sittin took the hint and left.

Lev came to see me for another reason. He wanted to hide his Party card with me, so that if the Germans moved in suddenly he would not be caught with it. Lev was one of the many Soviet citizens who had joined the Party not for ideological reasons, but because it was the only way to quick promotion. I knew he was sincere. He had two other requests: Would I give him a book, anything in German, which he could show to the first German soldier who discovered him? And would I lend him some civilian clothes to wear when the time came to discard his naval officer's uniform? His uniform had two high decorations, including the Red Star. I gladly gave Lev the clothes, but I had few books in German left. All I could give him was a volume of Heine which—as I warned him—would do him more harm than good with the Germans.

With September drawing to a close and winter moving in, the Soviet government declared Leningrad a "front." Every street was considered a potential battleground, heavily barricaded in a way which would have astonished those in the French Revolution. Military squads went from house to house, stripping them bare. Everything of metal or stone that was movable—bathtubs, radiators, slabs of stone—was ripped out and piled up into parapets.

By this time, all connections with the outside world had been cut off. The city was in a German noose. The next move was up to the Wehrmacht. All that stood between them and us were these barricades, some demoralized troops, and batteries of dummy guns. Already, the heavily defended cities of Smolensk, Kharkov, Kiev, and Odessa had been captured by the Germans, sometimes after a very brief fight.

We never found out why the Germans didn't move in. Probably what saved Leningrad was the difficulties they were having outside Moscow. Stalin insisted that most of the Soviet resources be concentrated on defending Moscow from invasion and, therefore, most of the German troops were sent there, too. Only a few German units, including the Spanish Blue Division, were left to besiege Leningrad and accept its surrender. Obviously the Germans never thought that the Soviet government would permit a city of 3,191,304 people (according to the 1939 census) to starve to death, so they sat at the gates and waited. Other conquering armies had made equally stupid mistakes.

When the Red Army and the government realized that the Germans would not make an all-out attempt to take Leningrad, we began to hear about our "heroic resistance" and the "bitter fighting" taking place nearby. We learned that the residents of Leningrad, true soldiers of the Soviet Union, had picked up guns and gone out to fight the invaders. This was quite a revelation to us! When we felt certain that there would be no German offensive, workers were ordered back to their jobs and students back to school. There was a general air of celebration as if we had weathered a storm. But in the somewhat phony rejoicing, no one noticed that while we were occupied with keeping the Germans out, starvation had crept in.

During October, the government cut our already small food rations, and the smaller the rations, the longer the lines were at food shops. Very often, after five to six hours of waiting, a customer would finally step inside only to learn that everything had been sold out. I certainly could not devote that much time to standing in line. Fortunately, I was able to eat at the Institute, but my ration card got used up there in exchange for microscopic portions, not enough to live on. I felt forced to supplement this meager diet with food from my reserves. I continued to save dried bread. but the fear that I would die of starvation was with me always.

For the average citizens, the black market became the only means of adding to their food supplies. Bakery workers sold extra bread at inflated prices, in small quantities so as not to be caught. In October, a pound of bread was selling at 140 rubles, while the salary of an average worker was 120 rubles a month. Those who did not have the money for extra food would sell part of their bread ration in order to trade it for other staples, especially fats. White collar workers who had sugar saved from better days traded it for bread. There was open barter in everything. During air raids people no longer went to the shelters but headed for food shops which might have been blown open by a near hit.

Looting became widespread. Looters would rush in, hardly noticing the dead or dying who might be lying about. Even the police took part, stealing from those who had stolen from someone else. I saw one policeman make a looter surrender some peas just taken from a bombed vegetable shop. What horrified me was that the peas were covered with blood, but neither the looter nor the policeman seemed to care. As food rations were steadily cut, we realized that we were doomed. We became fatalistic. We searched about for other sources of food. Drugstores were stripped of vitamin pills, glue, mineral oil, castor oil, hand creams, vaseline, glycerin—anything that the body could possibly absorb.

Early in October Leningrad was plagued with a "parachute scare." Everyone was searching for German parachutists who were supposed to have descended on the city. Late at night police officials would burst into an apartment and go from room to room looking under beds and in closets. This happened to me several times.

One night the police and the manager of our building found their "Nazis" in my apartment. Two good friends had come to visit and decided to stay overnight when it got too late to return to their homes. One of them, a Leningrad actor named Login, tried to prove that he was no parachutist. He produced his identification and argued eloquently on his behalf, but to no avail. The police arrested both men. As they were marched off, I noticed my next-door neighbor standing at her door, gloating. I learned later that she had informed the police that I had visitors. Two hours later, when my friends returned, I had the pleasure of thumbing my nose at her.

Whatever anger I had felt toward the building manager—and he had been spying on me for years—disappeared a few days later. One of the 105mm shells which were pouring into the city nightly caught him as he stood in the doorway of our building. It neatly sheared his head off. But after the first few minutes of hysterical excitement, the residents quieted down. We were already hardened to the sight of sudden death. Many people in Leningrad had been hit by shells by now and we had watched their remains being carted away. In this case, we paid a little more attention because the body lay in the apartment for nine days while his wife searched for wood to make a coffin.

Once she found enough, she set methodically to work, building it with our help. But when we delivered the body to the cemetery, we found the gravediggers would not bury it unless we gave them two pounds of bread. Their excuse was that they were too weak to dig and for proof they pointed to the many bodies lying at the cemetery gates. This shocked us, but later on we became accustomed to seeing the unburied dead.

For the living, life continued to be increasingly difficult. Electric trolley lines were shot down by artillery fire, leaving the cars stranded in the middle of the street. At first the government attempted to make repairs but after a while it gave up the struggle. It would have been foolish to string up new wires anyway. The Germans held Leningrad's second-largest power plant (the largest had been dismantled by the retreating Red Army). We were left with one small, old generating station, and it did not work full-time. Lack of coal forced the government to shut off all electric current in apartment houses, leaving most of the city in darkness.

I knew then that normal life in Leningrad would soon cease and I wanted to take a bath while I still could. The nearest public baths were on Karpovka street. I hurried there only to find a huge queue of women and children waiting their turn. Happy in the anticipation of my first bath in forty-five days, I joined them. Finally, as my turn approached, I began undressing, still in the corridor. Then, in the crowded, steamy room, so dimly lit I had to grope my way, I got the standard pail, filled it with water at one of the taps that lined the large room, dragged it to a bench and began soaping myself up. By the time I got to the showers, the hot water had been turned off. But this was only the beginning of my bad luck. The moment I had plunged my body under the stinging cold spray, an air raid alarm sounded. We all hurriedly finished dressing and made for the cellars. This was my last bath in Leningrad.

At the end of October I received another letter from Virginia, a letter of farewell. She told me that the fighting was rapidly approaching, and that she expected the Germans to arrive at any moment. It was a hopeless letter, mourning the fact that the son we both loved might be taken away from her. This letter was almost more than I could bear, leaving me half-crazed because I could do nothing for either of them. I was tightly sealed in, unable to leave a city that was slowly being strangled to death.

At about this time we got news that the Germans had been stalled again outside Moscow and we knew that our ordeal would be long and drawn out. We would have to endure a bitter winter without light or heat or food. Like wild people, the besieged citizens began to store up everything burnable. Park benches and picket fences disappeared. So did school benches. Any loose wood was gathered up. Books from libraries were hoarded for burning later.

The factories ceased operation, although oddly enough workers were still required to report every day and to remain on the site. The Soviet government was still afraid to permit even a little freedom. In the factory the NKVD could keep an eye on workers. The truth was that we were very far from any thought of revolution or even opposition. The war ceased to concern us. Food was the only thing on our minds—how to get it, what to do with it. Food and now, the need for warmth.

By early November, the government was no longer selling us anything but bread. Even this ration had been substantially cut down to 250 grams a day for laborers, and 125 for white collar workers. The 125-gram ration—the size of a pack of American cigarettes—was a soggy, heavy lump of bread. Every two days we could draw these rations and it became sort of a gauge of people's characters to see how they behaved. Most of them ate their two-day portion at once. Then, with no other source of food, they sat and starved until they could draw their next rations. Those who lacked basic self-control were the first victims of the Great Starvation.

The horrible days of slow death began in November, the days in which one friend after another succumbed to starvation and cold. November, that very cold November, brought us the first sight of bodies lying frozen in the streets, the bodies of people who, lacking the strength to move, stumbled and fell on the sidewalk and merely lay there, as if paralyzed. They became the prey of passersby who reached into their pockets and stole their bread cards. The victim would cry weakly, "Help me. My card has been stolen," and as we stood over them, powerless to help, we would see their life ebbing away. It was at this time that I began carrying a heavy stick.

What is more important—food or warmth? We struggled to keep the freezing weather out of our rooms. Artillery fire had shattered most of the windows in the city and through the holes in the makeshift replacements, lengths of stovepipe now emerged. A trade thrived in *burjuykas*, the small cast iron stoves which had been popular during the 1917 Revolution. Into them went whatever wood or paper could be gathered. I had no *burjuyka* but instead had a small kerosene heater and some kerosene which I carefully husbanded, using only a little in the morning to heat water and some in the evening to heat up my "supper."

In mid-November, I was assigned to a new job in the Institute, jamming German and Finnish broadcasts. Four of us worked there, one pair for twelve hours and then the other pair for twelve. My particular job was to handle the technical end. The signal to start jamming came from the NKVD headquarters, which monitored the enemy's propaganda programs. We were not sufficiently trusted to tune in ourselves, although the other three workers were all Party members. This job, though it took up a good part of my day and night, was worth a great deal to me because it gave me the right to hold a laborer's food card and freed me from other duties, such as digging trenches and drilling.

As the winter progressed, the bombings stopped. People dragged themselves along the streets more dead than alive, absolutely passive, unconcerned about the course of the war or their own future. Abandoned streetcars were torn apart by people seeking firewood. The houses showed gaps where artillery shells had struck them. And every day there were new horrors for us to witness.

Once, as I walked along Kirovski bridge, artillery shells suddenly whizzed by. A horse and wagon which had been plodding along fifty feet ahead of me just as suddenly became a mass of broken wood and torn flesh. But instead of running for cover, the people made a wild rush for the remnants of the horse, maddened by the sight of freshly killed meat. Soon there was a steady stream of women and men dashing away with pieces of bloody meat clutched to their chests. Over the larger chunks, women clawed and tore, trying to tear away what they could. In ten minutes, nothing was left of the horse. Even his blood had been sopped up. I had seen much since the siege began, but this was truly terrible for me.

That same night, I was a guest at Lala's home. It was still the same luxurious place and as I walked in I smelled a delicious and intoxicating aroma of roasting meat. Leningrad might be starving to death, but the NKVD took care of its own.

In the morning, on my way to the radio station in the Institute, I watched the sick, starving people making their way painfully to their offices and factories. The weather was getting colder and every day more dead bodies were found on the street—people who had not quite enough strength to make the useless trip by foot to work. Some had to walk six to ten miles and in their physical condition the exertion was too much. Luckily my apartment was only two blocks from my work. By the end of November even the government realized that it was needlessly condemning thousands to death and the order compelling all to report to their workplace was rescinded.

During the hours that I was free from the radio station, I still taught at the Institute. In the cold which now gripped Leningrad, it was necessary to wear a heavy coat, ear muffs, fur hat, and gloves in the classroom. My students, most of whom were girls, dressed the same way, making it difficult to tell male from female. My male students were all invalids or cripples—men the army had rejected.

One of them, a very nearsighted young man, always wrote with his head next to the paper. One day, at the end of my lecture, he did not straighten up. When one of the other students tried to rouse him, the boy turned out to be dead. But there was little sense of shock among us. By now death was a commonplace. No one had the strength to drag the corpse to the cemetery; it just lay with other bodies in the rear areaway.

Several days later we got a note from the student's mother asking what had happened to him. We wrote back that he was living at the Institute.

Shortly after that, the schools were closed, along with the factories and offices. Those of us who had any connection with the Institute kept returning, but not for classes. The cafeteria was still open and the building was a little warmer than the streets. That was enough to bring us back.

As the food situation steadily deteriorated, no animal was safe. Dogs and birds disappeared. So did mice. Cats had a regular market value of 700 rubles. Only the rats fattened—on human flesh. Meat was such a luxury that when my friend Professor Kiandsky invited me to his home to celebrate the birthday of his eight-year-old daughter Sonya, I was astounded to see tiny hamburgers on the table. After we drank the tea, sweetened with sugar I had brought, my friend took me aside. "Don't say anything to Sonya," he warned me. "But that meat we ate was her pet cat. We told her it ran away."

To make us even more desperate, we discovered a company of NKVD troops quartered at the Institute—fat, well-fed, healthy looking, well-armed men. Their sole duty was to keep an eye on us. We hated them from the start. They ate three times a day—not the thin gruel we were given, but big helpings of meat and *kasha*, a buckwheat porridge that was a staple of the Russian diet. They ate right under our noses and what they could not eat they permitted us to scramble over.

So far, we were almost without food, almost without heat, but we still had water. In the early days of December, this too was gone. As the mercury dropped, the water pipes burst in our apartments. Only in a few spots in Leningrad was there any running water—a few taps from which trickled the life-giving fluid. And around each tap every day was a mob of people. As a result, we were rationed on water: one pail a day, soon reduced to one kettleful.

For most people this was hardly enough. They began going down to the canals, breaking a hole in the ice and drawing out the dirty water. Some fell and froze to death on the spot, while others died dragging the heavy pails back to their homes. This trip to the canal became one more chore for me. But as usual, I felt impelled to build up reserves. One day I got hold of a sled, loaded it with every conceivable receptacle I could round up and went down to the Karpovka River to fill them up. But in the morning when I woke, I found that the water had frozen and burst all the glass containers.

From the start of the cold weather I had slept in my clothes. Now, as I lost weight I added other clothing. Soon I was wearing four or five pairs of socks, several pairs of trousers, several shirts. Every morning I would strip off my overcoat, do sitting-up exercises for a few minutes, and eat my breakfast—my quarter-ration of bread and some water, warmed only by the heat of my hands. Pretty soon I got used to taking a kettle of water to bed with me so that I would have a little water in the morning that was not frozen. By this time, of course, I had used up all my kerosene.

I kept the door of my room—which was also my "storehouse" of food—locked with three padlocks. But I was always afraid that someone would break in. One day it almost happened. Returning home, I found that Vanya, the fourteen-year-old son of our building's late manager, had broken two of the locks. Before he could break the third, he had died, and his body lay slumped against my door. I dragged the body over to his mother's room.

"He's not dead," she shouted. "He's not dead! He's only cold. I'll warm him up and you'll see."

She put the boy in her bed, covering him with every blanket she had, and that night she slept at his side, holding him to give him warmth. For a month she did this, crazed in her grief, refusing to believe that, not only her husband, but her son, too, was dead. Others kept their dead hidden in beds and in corners for more practical reasons. As long as the deaths were kept secret, the living could use their bread cards.

In spite of these constantly mounting horrors, we tried to maintain as much of the old life as possible, to live like human beings instead of like animals. Once a week, I would trudge across the ice of the Neva

River to visit my good friend Ludmila. I would bring a small amount of food from my sparse reserves and together with her pitiful share we would make a meal. On my weekly visits, I would break up enough firewood to last her for seven days. Then we would make a fire in her *burjuyka*, and I would indulge in the luxury of removing my overcoat. She lived in what had been a good house and there were plenty of wooden objects in the now-deserted neighboring rooms.

During these evenings, we would try to act as if Leningrad was not slowly dying, as if the city outside was the city we had known six months earlier. Because Ludmila liked poetry, we would sit near the stove after supper and she would read from her favorites, Gumilov and Yessenin, the lyric poets so hated by the Soviets. For a few moments the present would be forgotten. Then she would prepare a bed for me on top of a dining room table in one of the empty rooms—padding it with pillows and covering me with blankets. In the morning I would return to the terrible struggle.

That December, one of the coldest in Leningrad's history, the mercury dropped to forty-five degrees centigrade below zero. More and more people, weakened by hunger, would drop off to sleep as they sat down to rest for a minute and freeze to death. Yet the temptation to sit down and rest was irresistable. Those who did not die lost their food cards, and this was a more fearful kind of death.

There was no will and no water to fight the epidemic of fires which broke out now. Once a fire started in an apartment—usually from a *burjuyka*—nothing was done to stop it. It would rage until the house burned down. The occupants had no trouble finding another place to live; the death rate had done away with the housing shortage. But it was wise to find a brick house. Wooden ones were being torn down piece by piece to feed the *burjuykas*, and there was no telling when a building would collapse, occupants and all, because the lower floors had been stripped off by firewood hunters.

My daily diet in those days was a thin sliver of bread dipped in castor oil and toasted over a wood fire. When I had no castor oil I used fish glue. With this I drank several drops of eau de cologne diluted in water. And my imagination.

When one of my friends died, I found a cookbook among his effects and I induced his wife to trade it for four heavy volumes of mine, which made much better fuel. During the long evenings, I would read it, memorizing the succulent recipes, dreaming of the food I would one day prepare for myself. I even tore out the illustrations and mounted them on the walls. The book became an obsession.

Several days before the New Year of 1942, I ran into Professor Martian at the Institute. Unlike most people I knew, he seemed to be in fairly good shape. When he asked me to "celebrate" the holiday with him, I readily assented. On New Year's Eve, I made my way to his apartment, bringing some sugar and was quite surprised to find that his home was really warm. He was fortunate enough to have two rooms separated not by a wall, but by a huge, old-fashioned oven. Fortunately, he had put away enough wood to last for a long time. It was not a cheerful party for we had little to look forward to. Like most of the people in Leningrad, we made only one wish for the coming year. Solemnly we asked God to help us survive through January and February—the worst months of the year. We knew that once March came, there was a fighting chance for us to remain alive.

This meeting with Martian and the invitation to his apartment was a boon for me. When I described to him my room with its windows stuffed with paper and no heat, he invited me to sleep at his house. It took little urging and through the month of January I stayed with him, sleeping in the luxurious warmth of his second room, minus my overcoat and rubbers. Early in the morning, I would go to my place for breakfast. On my way through the streets, I passed what was becoming a typical Leningrad scene, women dragging sleds bearing their dead toward the cemetery, the bodies wrapped in old sheeting. But I knew that few of these corpses ever reached a burial ground. When the weary women thought no one was watching, they would dump the body anywhere and return home with an empty sled, their duty done.

My days followed a simple routine. I would get up at dawn so that I could get to the Institute in time to get a good place on the food line. This grew increasingly more difficult as members of the staff and students took to sleeping in the corridor outside the cafeteria, or even on the steps. The doors would open at 8 a.m. Mustering all our strength, and there was very little of that left in any of us, we would inch forward toward the kitchen. This was a process which took hours, and many would faint before they got to the bowl of warm water with barley which we called soup. With this in hand, we made our way cautiously to a corner, wary every second, fearing someone would snatch the bowl and swallow up the contents.

The most important people in our lives were the cooks and their assistants. It was in their power to give a slightly larger portion or to slip us an extra bowl of soup. Since the cafeteria ran out of food every day before the full line had been fed, it was vital to have someone in the kitchen who might put a little something away for you. Toward the end of the siege, the shortages at the cafeteria eased up, not because there was more food, but simply because many people did not have the strength to climb the Institute's three flights of steps. At this time, some of us were able to get second helpings regularly.

But although we were starving to death, the NKVD was still eating its fill. The practice of permitting the secret police to eat in our presence had been discontinued after several futile and pathetic attacks by students on the burly troops. In January, the NKVD took its meals behind locked doors, but we could still smell their food and see their leftovers.

Our life had descended to the most basic level. We were filthy and ragged, with a crazed look in our eyes. Differences between men and women had been totally obliterated. We hardly noticed that one by one our friends and acquaintances were dropping out of sight. We hardly noticed the piles of bodies lying stripped of their clothing on the back streets. As we limped along, each of us leaning on a cane, the only thing that seemed unusual was the sight of the Institute director, the commissars, and high Party officials, who continued to look like ordinary human beings. After a time, we even got used to that, as we got used to the blood-chilling, clunk, clunk, clunk of heads banging on the cobblestones as bodies were dragged away by feeble relatives who had not the strength to lift them up.

In this atmosphere of death, we unconsciously observed that it was the young and healthy who died first, then the able-bodied males, then the women. Curiously, the invalids and the tubercular, in most cases, were the very last to go. The number of the dead was legion. In December 1941, 53,000 died. In January, as record cold hit the city, 8,000 to 22,000 died daily, according to different sources. By June 1942, only 700,000 ration cards were issued for the entire city. By August 7, 1942, there were only 637,000 people left in the city. Even considering that about 350,000 had been evacuated and 200,000 soldiers died hopelessly defending the approaches to the city, that meant that as many as two million people died of starvation and cold—more than twice the casualties suffered by the United States and the United Kingdom in the entire war. Many of these deaths were still concealed by relatives in order to make use of their ration cards. In my apartment alone two bodies were concealed. People died silently, humbly, with no protest, as if this was the logical outcome of life in the Soviet Union.

But if the death rate for January was high, February brought a sharp increase. This was due as much to government inefficiency as to the weakened condition of the population. On January 31, when we applied for our next month's food cards, we were told that they were not ready, that we would have to apply the next day. For three awful days the people of Leningrad waited for their ration cards, and for three awful days they got the same excuse: there was no paper to print the cards. So the vast majority who had nothing put away and who lived on a day-to-day basis died. In these three days alone, that meant 150,000 people.

The macabre story of what some people did in those days may never be told. A friend of mine, a professor at the Institute, told me later that he began eating his carpet when the rations were cut off, neatly cutting out the greasy spots and cooking them. I was spared this measure of despair because I had saved my crusts of bread and could fall back on my reserves. But there were thousands who were not as fortunate as I.

Outright cannibalism broke out in February. Groups of wild

women began attacking and clawing at men in the street. We felt we
had hit bottom, but this was only the beginning. Bodies in the street
were dismembered by frantic residents. There were attacks on homes
with children. Kidnapping became commonplace and parents lived in
terror, afraid to permit their children to venture into the street.

One student of mine at the Institute brought his six-year-old
brother with him, his excuse being that there was no one to take care of
the child. Whenever anyone approached the boy, my student would put
his arms around his brother protectively and cry out, "No!" A few days
later the young man confessed to me that his parents were not dead,
but he believed that they had disposed of a three-year-old brother in
exchange for food. So he had moved out of his home, bringing the six-
year-old with him. One day the student died and his younger brother
disappeared without a trace.

Toward the middle of February, evacuations over frozen Lake
Ladoga increased, and I knew that if I pressed the matter, I could get
myself placed on a list of evacuees. My friend Professor Martian was
put in charge of a group of scientists leaving Leningrad, and he urged
me to come along. But I turned it down, not out of any feeling of hero-
ics but because I was sure that once I left the city I would lose contact
with my wife and son forever. I was not sure where they were, but I
knew that they could reach me in Leningrad. Martian was one of my
last friends and I hated to part with him. When he left, I moved my
bedding over to the Institute.

By the end of February, when Leningrad was a city of dead
bodies and living corpses, the government finally became convinced that
the people were not going to revolt. The NKVD troops, who had been
consuming the lion's share of the food that trickled in through the block-
ade, were removed and food stations set up to feed the starving. In
every plant, office building, and school these stations appeared, almost
as if they were administering first aid. One was opened at the Institute.

Three classrooms were set aside for this purpose. Two of them,
with sixteen beds each, were a sort of hospital, dividing the ambulant
starving and the bed-ridden starving. The third room was for the

corpses. Those admitted into either of the first two rooms were permitted to stay for ten days, being fed and looked after by a husky, dirty nurse. There was no time limit for the third room.

The first to be admitted into these "cure" rooms were the commissars, the directors of the Institute, and the Party functionaries—in short, those who needed it least. Following these came the essential workers, and due to my status as technician for the jamming station, I was admitted to the room for the ambulant starving. I still had to report for two hours daily work at the station.

The room was simply furnished: two rows of beds, a table at which we ate, benches, and a slop pail which was continually overflowing and which we took turns emptying. We were so weak that few of us were able to lift the pail and so it was dragged along, spilling on the floors of the room and the corridor.

Still, the accommodations were luxurious to us. Three times daily, we were served individual bowls of soup and rice. We were allowed some sugar, too. How then could we complain if the one stove in the room gave heat only to those in its immediate vicinity? Or if the smell of the slop pail permeated everything? What we did resent was that though we were now being fed almost adequately, the deaths continued. Every day one or two more would die, and ironically, it was the best fed who were first. The killer was dysentery combined with internal bleeding. When a man was struck by this, he was immediately taken off the regular diet and given tea and some pills at regular intervals, but this treatment never seemed to help.

My first four days were fine. I felt relatively fit and could work at the radio station. I even helped in the building of the bathhouse in the courtyard of the Institute. On the fifth day, the dysentery and bleeding began. The moment I reported it, I could sense a change in attitude toward me. I had been crossed off the list of the living. As my strength flowed out of me, there was a certain resentment in the manner of the staff, as if I was presuming by holding on too long. But though my condition was critical, I managed to remain conscious. Several times I was given injections and on the fourth day of my illness, the tea I was being given was stopped altogether.

I became obsessed then by two ideas: One, that I might be dumped in the room with the dead while I was still alive; the other, that my wife would not be able to find my body.

On the fifth day the nurse said to me: "You must understand, comrade, that other people are waiting for your bed." On the sixth day my student Karobin came to visit me.

"Is there any message that I can deliver to anyone in Leningrad?" he asked. "Can I write a letter to your wife telling her what happened to you?' There was no drama in his voice. It was a casual question, almost like asking me where I wanted my mail to be forwarded and this itself was a shock. I knew I was dying, but I was not prepared for death. I tried to be casual too.

"Thank you for your attention, but I really feel fine," I insisted. "See, I can even shake my head. Pretty soon I will be on my feet and we'll celebrate." But that night when I overheard that I would probably be dead in twenty-four hours, I decided to call Karobin back. The next morning he was at my bedside again.

"Take my comforter," I said to him. "Take it to my friend Clara Holmquist. I don't want it stolen when I die. Tell Clara that when she finds my family she must give it to my son."

Clara was that good friend of mine who, at the beginning of the German siege of Leningrad, had advised me to buy and store nonperishable foods as much as possible. She herself followed her own advice diligently.

The comforter was my dearest possession. It had been made for me by my mother when I was still a child, filled with the wool of the lambs I had tended myself on the slopes of Mount David in sunny Tiflis. It was my link with a happier past. I wanted my son to have it.

Karobin agreed. "But I can't carry it myself. I don't have the strength. I'll go tomorrow to your friend and give her your message. She'll come for it."

That night was a vigil for me, a long prayer for strength. I tried not to sleep, afraid that my life would slip away if I let go for a minute. I wanted to remain alive until I had given Clara the comforter.

Finally I fell asleep against my will. As I had feared, I was mistaken for dead and carried to a mass grave with other frozen bodies. In the meantime Clara went to the Institute to inquire of my condition. She was told that I already had died and was buried near her house. Passing the grave, carrying my comforter in her arms, she noticed a hand sticking out from the snow-covered ground. She also noticed a slight movement of the fingers. Feeling compelled to save whoever was still alive there, she quickly returned home and came back with her son Dzora, bringing along a shovel and a sleigh. They dug out the body and immediately recognized me. She put me on the sleigh and took me to her house, determined to bring me back to life.

After days of Clara's heroic efforts I opened my eyes. I was able to recognize her and Dzora standing by the side of my bed. This bed had clean sheets. My face and hands had been washed for the first time in many weeks. In the capable and gentle care of Clara's family (her brother was a pharmacist who was in a position to swap medicine for food and fuel), I slowly recovered my strength. Every day, Dzora would get my portion of soup from the Institute and this, together with what Clara provided, was enough to sustain my life. It was my good fortune that this compassionate, unselfish woman was now sharing with me the precious food that she had put away to keep her family alive.

One day, as I lay in bed, the loudspeaker in the apartment, which had been silent for a long time, suddenly sputtered to life with the loud strains of Bizet's *Carmen*. The government had decided to make death pleasant for us by playing records. In those days of my convalescence, it was a pleasure to sit with the family and listen to music which carried us back to a world we thought no longer existed. Reality was forgotten and with love and care, I returned to health.

During my illness the situation had improved. Large quantities of food were coming to the city over frozen Lake Ladoga, including the fabulous white bread which had been made from American Lend-Lease flour. Now there was chocolate in the stores, dried figs, margarine, even some meat. The bread ration was increased. Every day announcements were made of what would be put on sale the following day. Everyone made sure to be near a speaker to hear the welcome tidings for the morrow.

Although food was plentiful now, the horrors of the siege had not ended. People still continued to die, as if they had passed the point where an adequate diet could be of any use.

Early in March I felt well enough to venture back to the Institute to see my friends. A great change had come over the place. Very few of the people I had once known were still there. The food station had been shut down, the bodies removed, and the place cleaned up. Everywhere I went, I was greeted with: "Didn't you die?" or "Look, he's come back from the grave!"

Leningrad itself had changed. Although it was still very cold, we could feel spring in the air. On government orders all houses were being cleaned. Trucks roared through the streets, carting away the dead. Bulldozers were busy in the open fields excavating mass graves and covering over the deep pits full of the victims of the siege. Out of nowhere soldiers appeared to repair the streetcar lines. The resumption of air raids told us it was really spring. But the sound of dropping bombs seemed remote to us. We had known greater horrors.

On my next visit to the Institute, I learned that the army's mobilization board had ordered me to report. It was located at the Ksheshinski Palace, a beautiful building on the Kirovski Prospekt. A healthy-looking man in a Red Army uniform interviewed me.

"Comrade Keonjian, we want to congratulate you on your return from the dead," he said ironically. "Now you must do your duty for your fatherland at the front."

"Certainly," I said, "but this is only the second time I have been out since my illness. I'm so weak I can barely get around. And if I didn't have this stick to lean on, I wouldn't be able to stay on my feet."

"That's not my business," the man told me brusquely. "My job is to draft any man who can fire a rifle. You're strong enough to squeeze a trigger. Now go home and get ready to leave at a moment's notice. We'll notify you when you should report."

Weary and upset, I made my way back to the Institute to see if the director could do something for me.

"A group of Institute people are being evacuated on March 13," he told me. "It's a little late, but I'm sure I can add your name to the list." He gave me a note to present to the draft board. Again I dragged myself back to the Kirovski Prospekt and got a pass to leave Leningrad.

"They'll draft you wherever you go," I was told. "So it doesn't make any difference." This was on March 9. I had four days to dispose of all my personal effects, the furniture Virginia and I accumulated, and everything else. Four days in which to bid farewell to a whole period of my life.

My first idea was to turn all my belongings over to Clara so that she could use them until I returned—if I ever did. But this was impossible. The only way to move them to her house was on my back, and I did not have the strength. Then, because I needed money badly for my trip, I decided to sell what I could, leaving the rest to her. But by this time there was hardly anyone who had money or the interest to buy books and furniture. I realized that only the profiteers and black marketers could afford my things. So I approached a butcher who had been able to put away plenty of money in the early days of the famine. After bickering, we arrived at a price, 4,000 rubles and 200 grams of meat. (A bar of chocolate sold for 500 rubles at the time.) When the butcher refused to take my books, despite my assurance that they were worth more than the other things, I nearly wept.

The following day, Clara and her mother came to my apartment to help me pack up what I would take with me. I was allowed only four pieces of luggage, and I had a very difficult time trying to decide what to bring. I packed the most important of Virginia's and Karik's clothes in two valises. In the third I put my comforter and the precious cookbook. The fourth contained the most useless collection of unimportant objects and books and one could imagine. This last one I felt could be jettisoned if necessary. One final thing I took with me— my sack of dried bread, which I believed might be necessary. When I reached my journey's end in the Caucasus I was still clutching this sack.

By the time everything was set, it was 5 a.m. and I was half-frozen. Clara and her mother had long since gone home. They had arranged to meet me at the train, which was to leave at 2 p.m. So, without any sleep, I prepared my last breakfast—my last two ounces of "fresh" bread. I piled up those books which Clara had promised to take, added my two albums of records—Tschaikovsky's 5th and 6th Symphonies—and piled my belongings on a sled to make the long journey by foot to Leningrad's Finland Station.

The first half hour of dragging the sled was not too hard. After that my general weakness and lack of sleep began to tell on me. I stopped to rest and almost fell asleep. I continued down the street, stopping frequently, until I fainted. When I came to, I called for help, but no one paid any attention to me. Out of exhaustion, I fell asleep. When I awoke, it was 2 p.m. Horrified, I pulled myself to my feet and tried to run, but the strength just wasn't in me. Finally I was able to signal a truck bound for the station. I clambered in and soon reached my destination, only to find that the train with the Institute evacuees had already pulled out.

Dzora was still there waiting for me, although Clara had gone home feeling sure that we had missed each other in the crowd and that I was aboard the train. After being stopped from boarding other trains— I had no pass—I decided to return to Clara's with Dzora. I felt as if all the misfortune of the world had suddenly been heaped on me.

The next day I returned to the Institute to see if I could make new arrangements. But, with the old director gone, there was no one who knew me or cared to help. Instead, the new director told me sharply that I had been struck from the Institute's list. I was fired.

"I can't help you," he said in dismissal.

But my luck had not run out. Another teacher, a woman, had also missed the train and informed me that the Pedagogical Institute was being evacuated in less than a week. For two days she and I argued with this Institute's director, until finally we convinced him that we belonged on his list.

I did not realize then that I would never again see Clara, my angel of mercy. Years later I learned that she had survived the siege and died a few years after World War II.

This time, to make sure that I would not miss this train I got to the station the day before it was to leave. Our train, twenty summer coaches with broken windows, was closely guarded until the time came for us to get on board. Then there was a wild stampede. People were lifted bodily by the pushing crowd and thrown through the doors. Although we were packed like sardines, helter-skelter with our luggage, I had no complaints. I merely wanted the train to start. But from 4 p.m. until dusk, we sat in the station. At 8 p.m., we finally began moving out, to the joyous cries of the passengers. Throughout the night, we moved for a few minutes, then stopped, moved again, then stopped. We did not reach Lake Ladoga—thirty kilometers away—until the next morning.

When we did reach the lake, the command was shouted, "Everybody out." Cramped and cold, we descended to the snowy ground and the Red Army kitchens, where food was good and plentiful. All about us as we ate were cases—mountains of cases—of food waiting to be shipped into Leningrad. The letters on the cases were not Russian. Careful examination showed that the writing was English—Lend-Lease.

After we had been fed, a long line of trucks pulled up. A commissar called us together and announced: "These trucks will take you across the ice of Lake Ladoga. It is a dangerous trip and we want no one along who is panicky. If you are afraid, you should not go. The trip across the ice is two kilometers and there will be German planes." No one backed out. The commissar nodded.

That night, when we had piled in, thirty to a truck, the long convoy began to move onto the ice. It was like moving into the heavy traffic of a big city. There was a constant stream of trucks in both directions. Those going away from Leningrad carried refugees; those going toward Leningrad were stacked with cases of food and arms, but mostly with machinery.

We were well away from land when the German planes began to strafe us. I could hear the whine of the bullets, but none struck me or those next to me. Then bombs began falling. One shattered the ice in front of the truck ahead of us. Before its driver could react, he was under the waters of the lake.

We were told later that we had been on the ice an hour, but it seemed like a lifetime. On the opposite shore in the town of Voybokal were nurses waiting to treat those who had been wounded. Some had been killed outright by bullets; a few had died of heart failure. Those of us who were untouched were led to an army barracks to be fed the first regular meal we had eaten since the siege of Leningrad began: hot cabbage soup, meat, coffee or tea. For the children there were groats, powdered eggs, and bouillon—all American.

Then we began the real journey—to the North Caucasus, we were told, and for me this meant perhaps to my wife. Our means of transportation was a train of converted freight cars. They were so constructed that we could stand only in the center aisle. The boxcars had been divided in half horizontally on both sides of the aisle, forming two decks where we could lie, but not stand, and into these quarters we piled in. There were about forty people in each car, and for more than two weeks, we lived in these quarters.

It should not have been so bad. At every stop, we were well fed, with the kitchens organized and integrated so that the food was hot when we pulled in. But whether it was from the food or from the filth, amebic dysentery broke out, and death was once more with us. In my car alone, eleven died during the trip. Their bodies were just tossed off the train. On both sides of the tracks as we rode along, we spotted more dead bodies, thrown from earlier trains.

By the time we reached Stalingrad, the snow was gone and it was really spring. Once again we could see green earth and growing things. And though we were surrounded by our own filth and many of us were sick, this sight suddenly made us realize that the city of death where we had lived for close to nine months was far away. There was reason to be hopeful.

When we reached Mineral'nyye Vody, our destination in the North Caucasus, 960 miles away, janitors and male nurses surrounded our train, which had been shunted into an isolated area surrounded by a high wire fence. Masked and gloved to prevent further infection, the janitors removed the very ill. The rest of us were hurried past the fences, where the curious stared at us in horror, to delousing chambers and a steam bath. For the first time in many months, I removed my filthy clothes, then handed them in to be disinfected. As I tried to take off my shirt, pieces of it stuck to my skin, and pieces of skin came off with it. Then we luxuriated, three to a shower, under steaming hot water.

I had forgotten what my naked body looked like, but the sight now was not pretty—swollen ankles, body skeletal except for a pot belly, skin peeling off. I could feel my long beard and unshorn hair. I looked about me. The other men were much the same. And here and there, I spied a woman showering with us. But none of the men paid her any heed, nor she them. Against my will, I was pushed away from the wonderful water. There were others in line waiting their turns. As I left the shower room I was handed my disinfected clothes, then assigned quarters.

I lay on my bunk clean and elated. Now I knew that I had survived the terrible ordeal. Despite freezing cold and starvation I had been able to pull through. I was alive. An old Russian proverb says "Zhizniye silneye smerty"—"Life is stronger than death." I would be well again. I would find my wife and child and we would build a new life together.

The Badayev wardhouses in flames. (Sovfoto)

A woman dragging a dead body wrapped in a sheet on a child's sled. (Sovfoto)

A woman draws a starvation weakened man on a child's sled. (Sovfoto)

Abandonned make-shift coffins on the street. (Sovfoto)

The "Ice-road" through the frozen Lake Ladoga. (Sovfoto)

Clara Holmquist, my rescuer in Leningrad.

FOUR

*A*fter searching several hospitals, Virginia found me at last in Mineral'nyye Vody in the northern Caucasus, but she hardly recognized me. She was shocked to see how I had changed—how old and feeble I looked. It is amazing that I survived that ordeal, that anyone did. It is also amazing that so many of us in Leningrad were able to keep working for so long, despite the fact our brains and bodies were starving. I think the discipline of going to the Institute each day, of trying to keep to a routine, saved my life, and I was much too stubborn to give up, as so many people did.

By the time Virginia located me, I was able to stand and walk slowly with the help of a cane. She checked me out of the hospital and rented a small, one bedroom hut. Her mother joined us and we started to get back to a "normal" life. Karik, now almost six years old, was well, but I could tell he'd already been affected by the trauma of the war. He did not laugh the way he used to. His childhood was already over.

I felt I had been out of touch with the world for a long time and was eager to catch up on the news of the war. That summer of 1942 was probably the grimmest time for the Allies. German troops were still occupying the Ukraine, Lithuania, Estonia, and western Soviet Russia, as well as France, Norway, and the Low Countries. Germans were outside Moscow and Leningrad and were advancing toward Rostov/Don and Stalingrad. U.S. troops were just beginning to get mobilized. War production in both the U.S. and U.S.S.R. lagged pitifully behind that in Germany.

I heard the war news only in bits and pieces. I knew there were several fronts—in Eastern Europe, Italy, North Africa, and in the Pacific, although that war seemed to belong to another world. I had no idea of the great losses of the Soviet army. Stalin was using everything he could to whip up patriotism so Soviet citizens would be willing to make the sacrifices that a major land war entailed. Only much later did I learn that Soviet military casualties already approached two million. Hundreds of thousands of people had fled Moscow and as many had left the Ukraine. Most had moved east of the Urals and now hundreds of new factories were being built there as fast as the materials could be assembled. Eventually these factories would turn out the thousands of tanks and aircraft necessary to defeat the German army.

Any notion of security or safety that we might have had in Mineral'nyye Vody evaporated quickly in the summer of 1942. We heard that German tanks were advancing toward us on their way to Rostov. Strangely, although rumors ran up and down the streets of the town, residents showed no sign of fear. In fact, people were preparing to welcome the invaders. Some Jews even refused to join the retreating Soviet Army, thinking their chances were better with Germans than with their native countrymen. They had no idea what was in store for them. Soviet propaganda had not given them any warning about the danger they might face at the hands of the Nazis. The Nazi Party claimed that Slavs were subhuman and good only for menial work. When this realization reached the millions of Slavs in the lands occupied by the Germans, no one any longer expected good treatment from the Third Reich.

I thought often of an old Soviet joke that asks, what is the difference between a pessimist and an optimist? A pessimist is a person who says that everything around him is bad. An optimist is a person who believes that in the future nothing could be worse than it is now. In 1942 there were many such "optimists."

For a while we found ourselves in limbo. Soviet troops had retreated and with them a large part of the town government. The Germans seemed in no hurry to move in. The population took advantage of the situation and began cleaning out the government stores and warehouses. At one point we learned that a huge amount of beluga black caviar was being stored in one of the warehouses. This was a rare commodity, designated for high party officials who vacationed in the town.

Looters brought out huge barrels of caviar and rolled them down the streets. Some of the barrels split open and the precious product spilled out onto the sidewalks. Immediately people filled jars, bowls, cups, and any other containers they could find, scooping up the caviar from the ground.

Virginia, too, filled a large jar and rushed home to hide it in the basement. Later, a rumor spread that the German would confiscate the valuable stuff as soon as they occupied the town. I was determined to keep this treasure, however, knowing that would be better for my recovery than any medicine. I dug a large hole in the basement to store both the caviar and my radio set, not stopping to consider what would happen to them underground. When I dug them up three months later, both were ruined—the caviar was rotten and the radio completely rusted.

Mazut or black oil was almost as precious as caviar. One of our distinguished professors, Rukovishnikov, in a heroic act of charity, climbed onto a huge mazut tank abandoned in the center of town. His plan was to dip into the tank with his pail and then empty his pail of black oil into the containers held by the crowd standing below him. It almost worked—his aim was off by only a fraction, but that fraction was whipped by the wind until most of the people waiting with their cups and jars were covered top to bottom in the black oil. For a change, we got to laugh at ourselves!

Finally, in mid-July 1942, the Germans entered our town. I did not know it then, but Sevastapol had just fallen to the Germans after a nine-month siege and Soviet troops were abandoning Rostov to the conquerors. In Mineral'nyye Vody, the entire population was on the streets as the Germans marched in. Young girls dressed in their best outfits with their arms full of flowers smiled and waved their welcome. Some of them even jumped on the tanks to kiss the drivers, riding with them for a block or so. The drivers were young, probably eighteen to twenty years old, and freshly recruited for the Eastern front.

They warned us that they were not the main contingent of the occupying army. The next wave would come in a few days and would consist of the Gestapo and the military police. Still, such warning meant little to most of the population, who remained hopeful.

After a few days, when the occupation was complete, I went to the German command headquarters to get a pass to go to a nearby town. I couldn't believe my eyes when I saw who was issuing the passes. It was the same Soviet official who had been there before. The same man, occupying the same position, and doing the same job as when the Soviets were in charge! Soon I found out that all those in the local government or militia who did not evacuate the town were now employed by the Germans. The Germans claimed that they had no choice but to rely on those who already knew the town. That may have been true, but it seemed very odd to me that the Soviet functionaries were so eager to get on the payroll of their victorious enemy. Not many Frenchmen chose to do so.

For their part, the Germans organized food distribution centers in town to supply the civilian population with a minimum ration. Families with children were entitled to a quart of milk a day. That small gift kept my family alive.

Eagerly we read the newspapers published by Germans in Russian for the occupied Soviet territory, searching for information on the course of the war. We knew very little about the movements of either German or Soviet troops, but we understood that Stalingrad on the Volga River was a key point for both. We didn't learn the full story until much later. General Friedrich von Paulus, leading 500,000 troops (which included Italians, Hungarians, and Rumanians, as well as Germans) marched toward the city. The defenders were General Vasili Chuikov and the Second Soviet Army. General Georgii Zhukov, who had led the victorious counter-offensive of Moscow, joined him with more troops.

All summer the troops massed and skirmished, preparing for a major battle. It finally began on September 13, when the Germans entered the city. The battle that followed was one of the bloodiest and most desperate of the entire war. Fighting was block-by-block, even room-by-room, as Germans crawled forward and Soviets pushed back. Chuikov had spent the summer overseeing the mining of city buildings and had set up sniper nests in every available crawl space. Now his planning was paying off, as German casualties mounted.

On November 19, Zhukov launched an offensive. With six armies, he encircled von Paulus' army. Von Paulus wired Hitler, requesting that the German army be allowed to break out. Hitler refused, insisting that the army must stay and hold Stalingrad. This was a serious error on his part. The German army was now blockaded, under siege. Their food stores became depleted, and the bitter winter caught them without adequate clothing.

On January 31, 1943, von Paulus surrendered his entire army— only 91,000 men were still alive. This was a turning point of the war. From this point on, although we did not know it, the Germans were in retreat and the Soviet army was on the offensive.

Even before that, in late December, we realized that the Germans must already be encountering difficulties in the Caucasus because of the number of retreating regiments that passed through our town. They methodically removed the telegraph and telephone poles and disassembled the railroad tracks in a desperate attempt to slow down the advancing Soviet troops. We didn't know what that would mean for us, and we waited nervously, not having much else to do but to gather kindling and chop tree branches for our wood-burning stoves (*burjuykas*).

On December 31, 1942, we were notified that the Germans would begin withdrawing from Mineral'nyye Vody and would take with them all able-bodied civilians to work in their slave labor camps, as *ostarbieters* (eastern workers) or OSTs. These camps were located in various places in Eastern Europe, and the OSTs, as well as prisoners of war, were forced to work long hours in the factories for the Nazi war machine.

Sometime past midnight on January 1, 1943, Virginia and I were awakened by German soldiers bursting into our room, shining flashlights in our faces, and shouting "*Schnell! Schnell!*" Although we expected such an invasion, it was still a shock and we reacted slowly, which caused us to be abused further. At last, shivering in the cold night air, we climbed aboard the truck already loaded with forced evacuees. We had decided earlier that if we were forced to leave, we would leave Karik with Virginia's mother, who was not scheduled for deportation because of her age.

That was a logical decision, made after mature deliberation, because we did not know where we would be going or what horrors awaited us. However, as we crowded into the bed of the truck and it began to rev its engine, Virginia's heart overruled logic. She burst into tears and insisted that she would not be separated from her child, no matter what. Then she called out to her mother to toss Karik to us, on the already moving truck. Otherwise, we probably would never have seen him again. We knew that at least we were together. That is all we knew.

The trucks proceeded toward Rostov/Don, driving all night. The city, once Virginia's home, showed the damage of the recent battle there. We were transferred onto a freight train, which was already full of deportees. It also held a large number of wounded German soldiers, returning home. As we continued west, Soviet airplanes bombed and strafed the train, but no more than a dozen people were killed—a small number to me after the carnage I had seen. Many were wounded, but not too seriously.

Nothing would stop this train. We could feel its determination as we rumbled along. Whenever a section of track was destroyed by a Soviet bomb, it was repaired almost instantly by German engineers. Other, similar trains were moving across the Ukraine, also full of human cargo. Many passengers were *"Folks Deutch"* or Russian Germans, who had lived unmolested in Russia for generations. Now they were in fear for their lives—not from the Germans, but from the advancing Soviet troops. Stalin had already deported large numbers of them to Siberia.

At practically every stop along the route we were well fed at field kitchens. That proved again to me the German organizational talent, which allowed them to feed warm food to a huge group of people under appalling conditions.

Eventually our train arrived in Warsaw, where the passengers were sorted out and sent to different locations. Civilians like us were sent to the eastern frontier of Germany, to a redistributing camp, prior to being sent to an OST camp. There we were given a section of the cold, dingy barracks. By stringing up blankets we managed a small measure of privacy.

I was still not in robust health, and almost at once I became quite ill. An Ukrainian doctor, another displaced person (or DP) like us, treated me. Almost every evening he would drop by our quarters to check my health and to chat. He didn't speak a word of German and often asked Virginia to interpret something or translate a short sentence from Russian into German, which she did gladly. Her German, learned as a child, was virtually perfect.

After about a month at the redistribution center, suddenly in the middle of one night the Gestapo burst into our barracks. Without explanation Virginia, Karik and I were herded onto a train and taken to Berlin, still almost untouched by Allied bombs. Virginia and Karik were detained at the railroad station and I was taken to Gestapo headquarters, where about eight high-ranking officers in full uniform were assembled. They began interrogating me in Russian about my background. I felt I had nothing to hide and answered each question as pleasantly as I could, smiling at my interrogators, although I did not like the smirks on their faces. As soon as they had an answer, one of them would call the Gestapo agent at the railway station and compare my answer with Virginia's. She was being interrogated there by other Gestapo agents.

I was repeatedly asked the names of professors at my Institute in Leningrad. These names were carefully checked with the names on their own list. If I forgot to mention someone's name, they immediately pounced on it, asking why I dropped so and so. Did I have any reason for it?

"Would it be easier for you to speak in Yiddish?" someone asked.

"No," I replied. "I am an Armenian, not a Jew."

Then one of the agents said scornfully in perfect Armenian,

"You claim to be an Armenian. Do you still remember that language?" When I answered, also in perfect Armenian, the smirks on the faces of the interrogators disappeared.

After we exchanged a few words in Armenian, the agent who had spoken in Armenian asked me to step out into the hall with him for a moment and he would try to clear this matter up with the others. As he ushered me out into the hall, he told me that he now believed I was an Armenian and not a Jewish spy, as someone in my camp had alleged. He would try to convince the others of my true identity, he said. "But," he added ominously, "I cannot guarantee that I will succeed."

This was the first time I knew what crime I was being charged with. Then my new confidante advised me that I was already scheduled for execution that same afternoon. My smile vanished and I began to shake with fear.

"Who named me as a Jewish spy?" I asked, trembling. He told me it was the Ukrainian doctor, who had so selflessly treated me during my illness. Shocked, I immediately realized that all those translations that Virginia had so graciously supplied were helping him to compose in German my dossier for the Gestapo. Feigning kindness, he had actually condemned me to death. Then I remembered that the doctor had had several gold rings on his fingers, probably rewards for betraying other DPs before me.

The interrogator went back into the conference room, leaving me to sweat and shiver. A half-hour later he emerged, smiling. He had vouched for my innocence and the others believed him. "But," he said forcefully, "if they ever find out you lied, they'll shoot us both." I didn't doubt it. He also confessed that he was not a Gestapo officer at all, but an Armenian tobacco merchant living in Berlin, and that the Gestapo had recruited him, dressing him in uniform to try to trap me.

(Many years later, in 1959, I revisited Berlin and made a point of finding this man who had saved my life. I asked him to take me to the place where I was scheduled to be executed. It had become a beauty parlor. All trace of the one-time police state had disappeared.)

After my identity was satisfactorily established, the Germans moved us to a camp in Goblenz, Czechoslovakia, which was still occupied by German forces. Nearby was a factory where camp residents were dismantling Allied aircraft that had been shot down and assembling various types of electronic and mechanical gears.

Virginia and I were sent to work in this factory. As we learned later, the Gestapo continued to investigate my background, hoping they would find some evidence of my "true" identity. They were still suspicious. My name was announced at many German slave labor camps, POW camps, and even in some concentration camps, with the request for anyone who knew me personally to come forward.

One day a starving POW named Serge Shachparonian weakly raised his hand and whispered that yes, he knew an Edward Keonjian who was the son of a doctor who took care of him in Tiflis, Georgia, when he was a boy. Serge was immediately taken from the camp and flown to the Gestapo headquarters in Berlin, where he was thoroughly interrogated. They believed him. Not only did he clear my identity at last, he saved his own life. He was never returned to the POW camp and thus avoided starvation.

Instead, he was brought to my camp so I could identify him. I recognized him at once as a classmate from my Armenian school in Tiflis. (Much later, I sponsored his immigration to the United States. He subsequently married and moved to Los Angeles, where he died in 1982.)

This was now the early spring of 1943. Life in the labor camp became routine over the next two years as the war raged around us. There were thousands of these small camps throughout Germany and Eastern Europe. All able-bodied German men were in the military, and someone had to produce the war materiel. As many as two million foreign nationals were conscripted to work in such factories. Because Virginia and I were Caucasian rather than Slavic, we received somewhat better treatment than other Russians. The work in our camp was not hard, and the food was adequate, although the hours were long

Holidays and birthdays were an especially poignant time for us, but somehow we always managed to find some trinket to give Karik and tried to celebrate with the other inmates. Germans are very sentimental about Christmas. They decorated Christmas trees and filled the air with carols on Christmas Eve.

There were a few other children for Karik to play with. Virginia had already taught him both alphabets (Russian and German) and some arithmetic. We could tell that he was very bright and often talked to him as if he were an adult rather than a child. He was an outgoing little boy with a beautiful smile.

One Sunday when the children were playing outside the barracks, a German woman shouted to Virginia with horror in her voice, "Your child hit my son!"

Virginia responded that she was sorry. "Unfortunately, often children hit each other when they play," she pointed out.

"You do not understand," the woman insisted. "Your son hit a *German* boy!" Apparently that was an especially outrageous occurence and required profound apologies.

Because of her excellent German, Virginia became acquainted with the wife of the camp commandant and the two would occasionally chat about the war. One day by accident I noticed my own book among the other Russian books brought by the Germans from Soviet libraries. These books were being used as fuel, to heat the barracks. The commandant had learned about the book as well and began to take a special interest in me. Virginia was very careful about what she said to the commandant's wife and how she said it. She agreed that, yes, in the Soviet Union I had been engaged in radio communications, but she never gave any indication that I was still interested in radio technology.

However, I definitely was. While no one was watching, I managed to build a primitive radio set from discarded electronic parts. I was taking a big chance, because if caught I would probably be executed on the spot. However, my desire to know what was happening on the front was overwhelming, overshadowing any need for safety.

I was not able to secure a set of regular earphones for the set. Therefore I hooked it up to a small speaker made of rolled paper attached to an earpiece from a discarded telephone. In order to keep our radio a secret and not to attract anyone's attention with its strange noises,

Virginia and I took turns hiding under the blankets with an ear pressed close to the set in the late nights when the BBC program was on. The other would stand look-out.

One night while I was listening, I was dumbfounded to recognize the voice of my own cousin, Victor Armbarzumian, speaking from England! His was a typical anti-Nazi speech, directed to German soldiers, urging them to surrender. Why he, a world-renown astrophysicist, was used for this kind of propaganda still puzzles me. I wonder if his words had any effect on the troops—or if they even listened.

Listening to the BBC on that primitive radio set, I learned of Stalin's call for a Second Front in Eastern Europe. Churchill and Roosevelt seemed to be concentrating their resources in Western Europe, and Stalin began demanding that the Soviet Union receive more aid. Nonetheless, the liberation of France came first. On June 6, 1944, D-Day, Operation Overlord was launched by the Allies. More than two million troops in 4,000 transport ships, 800 warships, and innumerable small craft invaded the coast of Normandy over a twenty-four hour period. The fighting was ferocious and a half-million men were wounded or killed. Over the next three months, Allied soldiers worked their way toward Paris, finally liberating that city on August 25, 1944. Now, at last, the Germans were in retreat.

In July, in southern Europe, the Allies invaded Sicily. After another bloody fight, in August the Americans took Messina and ninety percent of the town was destroyed. They began driving Mussolini's troops off the island. As the Allies moved into Italy and toward Rome, the Italian government surrendered on September 3, 1944. One-third of the Axis powers had been defeated.

The Germans continued to retreat on the Eastern Front. On September 28, 1944, the Soviet Army, advancing to the west, entered Czechoslovakia. Soon we could hear the blast of their artillery. Tension increased in the camp. We had no idea what would happen to us. Would the Germans move us farther west? Or would we fall into the hands of Soviet troops? Neither option was good.

One evening the camp commandant came to see me. He was

Swiss and a fanatic Nazi as well. He left his native land to help the
German "just cause." He told me that he would never permit me to fall
into the hands of the Soviets—I was much too valuable a "trophy" because of my engineering background. Therefore, he said calmly and dis-
passionately, he would kill me and my family, as well as himself and his
family, if the Soviets surrounded the camp.

"So do not worry," he added very seriously.

Virginia and I looked at each other in horror. We knew we
would have to do something drastic.

Later that night, as soon as we were alone and Karik was asleep,
I told Virginia that I thought the commandant was crazy enough to kill
us and she agreed. "We have to try to escape," I insisted. "We have to
take our chances." Again she agreed.

Our barracks were located on a small hill. It was now winter
and snowing heavily. We bundled Karik up in a blanket and sneaked
outside. The camp was not heavily guarded because they knew there
was nowhere for us to go—we were in enemy territory, surrounded by
people who would probably turn us in. Cautioning Karik to keep quiet,
we pushed him down the hill, so he would slide to the bottom. Virginia
went next and I followed. Reunited at the bottom of the hill, we asked
each other, "What now?"

We decided to look for railroad tracks and follow them until
we reached a town or station. After about twenty minutes of trudging
through the heavy snow with teeth chattering, listening intently for any
sign that our absence had been detected, we finally dug out the tracks
out of the snow. We had to be sure we were following the tracks west,
not east. The constant artillery roar was a good indication of which
direction was east.

We turned west, away from the sounds of battle, and continued
through the ever-deepening snow for about an hour. We finally reached
a small depot with a single person inside, the stationmaster. Virginia
asked about the next train—would it be stopping here and could we get
a boarding pass?

One glance at our shabby appearance made the station-master

immediately suspicious. He demanded to see our papers. For a moment we thought that was the end of our freedom. But before he could reach for the telephone, Virginia shouted at him in perfect German, "You swine! How dare you ask for identification from a German woman!"

She knew well the German mentality. He immediately apologized and issued us passes. Ten minutes later the train arrived and we were on our way to the west. Just where were we going? We had no idea. The sky was lightening and soon it would be daylight. We wanted to put as much distance as we could between us and the camp.

At each stop, more people like us—runaways from camps and German civilians fleeing from the advancing Soviet troops—got on board. We heard their stories, told haltingly in anger and disgust. Soviet soldiers were committing atrocities in each village they entered. They raped women and young girls, and looted houses, shooting the residents who tried to resist them. They did not hesitate to cut off the hands of people, living or dead, to get their wristwatches and jewelry. My little family drew closer together on the hard train seat, holding on to each other. We would not let the Soviets get us.

Other trains full of refugees joined ours. We heard more stories. On February 13 and 14, the Allies had fire-bombed Dresden. The city was teeming with hundreds and thousands of Selisian refugees. An estimated 135,000 persons perished. We were dumbfounded. Why did they attack this open city? It had no military installations and was known throughout the world as a cultural center, with priceless museums and monuments. To destroy works of art seemed both senseless and ruthless, not to mention the lives of innocent people.

Later the Allies claimed that their target was railyards on the outskirts of town. However, in reality, they were aiming at the city center, which was bombed extensively, including the Semper Opera and the Zwinger Palace. Certainly these landmarks were recognizable from the air.

By February 1945, it was obvious that the Third Reich was collapsing. Yet, as usual, German field kitchens with hot meals were assembled all along the tracks, feeding everyone at no charge. Some

Armenians who had escaped the camps were also on our train. They were heading toward Rottweil, a small town in the Black Forest region of Germany, where they heard that the mayor was sympathetic to Armenians. Lodging was available there, so they said. We decided to go with them.

Some talked about escaping to Switzerland, only forty kilometers away. A short swim across the Boden Zee was all that was necessary. However, the Swiss actively protected their neutrality and did not hesitate to shoot anyone trying to get into their country. A few escapees we knew did try that route and were turned back by the fire from Swiss patrols.

Going to Rottweil was another good move for us. There were many vacant barracks in town and we were given a room right away. Only months later, in April 1945, Rottweil fell into the hands of the French-Moroccan occupation army. As their tanks rolled into town along the main street, I noticed a German woman on the other side of the street, completely undisturbed by the commotion, cutting and distributing bread coupons, as if she were a thousand miles away from war. Another was busily polishing the door knob on her front door, her back to the street. German discipline under any circumstances! (*Ordnung must sein.*)

In one of the town's streets there was a small German coffee shop where customers could also get a glass of beer. An unshaven man in rags, with sunken eyes, limping on one foot, dragged himself into the coffee shop and, whispering, asked for a glass of beer. He had just returned from the POW camp in Russia. He looked awful. He paid for his beer, the exact amount requested by the owner of the coffee shop, and left without saying another word.

"Who was that man?" I asked the owner.

"My brother," answered she, without any trace of emotion.

While the fighting was still going on, shrapnel from the French artillery hit a shoe store in town and scattered shoes all over the street. Everyone rushed out to get a "free" pair of shoes. I scooped up a pair and happily brought them home. They were my size all right, but both shoes were for the left foot. Strangely, a month later, the owner of the shoe store walked into our room and said, "I noticed that you took a pair of shoes without paying for them. Please pay me now!"

(Even stranger, forty years later in the United States, I attended a party in Boston. Our hostess began telling of her experiences in Rottweil during the war, when the French occupied the town. She described the shelling of the shoe store. "I picked up a pair of men's shoes from the street," she continued, "but unfortunately both shoes were for the *right* foot!" When I told her my story, we laughed with delight over the coincidence.)

To our dismay, the Moroccan soldiers were no better than the Soviets. They were called Goums and were known for their stealth and skill with a knife. They were constantly on the prowl, seeking houses to loot and women to rape. One morning a group of four or five Moroccans broke into our room and waved a gun at Virginia, threatening to rape her. Suddenly they stopped their advance. One of them had noticed a ring on Virginia's finger. I had given it to her years before and its stone contained inscriptions from the Koran in Arabic. They fell to their knees in front of her, whispering in Arabic, then got up and abruptly left.

A few minutes later we heard a single gunshot on the street. The Moroccans returned with a bicycle, presenting it to Virginia with an apology for their behavior. They had taken the bicycle by force from its German owner and then shot him dead.

Suddenly, after six years, the war was over. Hitler was dead. Peace in Europe was declared on May 8, 1945. There were wild celebrations in New York, Paris, and Moscow, but we did not celebrate. We were relieved that the war was over, but we were frightened about what lay ahead.

As more displaced Armenians continued to arrive in Rottweil, the French authorities decided to put all of us, almost 400 people, in one of the liberated camps. Most of us were professionals—scientists, doctors, artists, clergymen, and so forth. We all categorically refused to return to the Soviet Union. We knew that because we had been exposed to the Western world, we would be considered potentially dangerous to the Soviet state, even as DP camp inmates. We would be isolated from the rest of the population and sent to a Gulag in Siberia. The infamous Yalta agreement, signed by Winston Churchill, Franklin Roosevelt, and Josef Stalin, specified (on Stalin's insistence) that those who refused repatriation should be deported by force. Stalin needed more slave labor forces for his Gulag.

Thus, the most shameful phase of the postwar period began. Hundreds of thousands of former inmates of German camps were loaded like cattle on Allied trucks. If these innocent people, who were merely refusing to return home, balked at the order, they were brutally beaten by Allied soldiers and shoved into the trucks to be delivered to the Soviets. These scenes of screaming women and children trying to jump out of the trucks, sometimes actually leaping out and falling under the wheels of the moving vehicles, killing themselves, will never be forgotten.

Among the Armenians at the camp were ten to twelve musicians. Occasionally they entertained the French soldiers and officers to gain their favor. One day when they were playing in a hall, Soviet soldiers burst in, arrested the musicians, and took them away. None of the French officers rose to protest, although this happened in their sector.

The musicians were put on an open railroad freight car attached to a train moving east. When the train began rolling, the Soviet soldiers forced the musicians to play patriotic songs to show their "happiness" about being repatriated. However, as the train moved east, some of the musicians managed to slip off the car. On the third day of the journey, very close to the Soviet occupation zone, only three musicians remained. Finally they too dropped out. The KGB officer in charge of the group must have realized that his days were numbered. He also jumped off the train and joined the trio disappearing into the woods. Eventually he showed up in Rottweil with the others and became another DP.

In order to avoid forceful deportation, we Armenians decided to become "Iranians," taking advantage of the fact that we did not look Slavic. We notified the French military authorities that we were Iranian merchants who had been caught in Germany during the war. We requested the authorities to get in touch with the Iranian consul who would help us get the proper travel documents so we could return to our beloved native land. We knew that it would take a century for the French to find an Iranian consul and another century for him to reach us, so we were buying time. We erected a small mosque in the middle of our camp and knelt before it five times a day. We also wore Iranian symbols on our clothes—a lion in front of the rising sun.

Both the French and the Germans were confused, not knowing what to do. Why did our children speak Russian? they asked. Ah, we'd answer confidently, because Iran had a long border with Soviet Russia, it was common practice to teach our children this language first, as a sign of respect for our great neighbor to the north. Although this explanation sounded far-fetched, the French and Germans were relatively easy to fool. It was a different matter with the Soviet authorities.

When the Soviet Repatriation Committee visited our camp, they were not impressed with the Iranian story. "These are our people and we are going to get them back," the chairman told the French authorities. Fortunately, we had an informer in the French *commendature*. The consul's secretary, a German girl, promised to let us know when to expect the arrival of the Soviet soldiers and their trucks.

Early one morning our informer told us that the next day the Soviet trucks would be in town to "collect" us. We had just enough warning to tear down our mosque, destroy the Iranian symbols, pack up our meager belongings and disperse into the nearby woods and hills. Some found shelter on German farms, some put up makeshift tents, constantly moving from one place to another. When they discovered our disappearance, the Soviet authorities promised to pay French gendarmes a reward for each so-called Iranian delivered to them. That was the beginning of a year-long manhunt.

The gendarmes were primarily looking for men, because men brought a higher reward. So with the blessings of my family, I escaped alone to the American zone of occupation without an ID. A few weeks later, I crossed the border illegally again, this time on a borrowed motorcycle to pick up Karik, who was by then seven years old. It was a child's motorcycle and I'm sure I looked laughable, with my long legs draped around it, trying to keep them off the ground. I attached a Red Cross flag to the front and invented a story about being a doctor on my way to an emergency in case I was stopped at the border. As it turned out, that wasn't too far-fetched. Karik, seated precariously on the front of the motorcycle, was running a high fever and I raced to get him back to the German family who had agreed to house us for a while.

A month later, I was able to bring Virginia across. We had made plans to meet on such-and-such a date, at midnight under a certain bridge. I was there at the appointed time, on my little motorcycle. She was not. I waited a while, then finally called out her name in a whisper. Gradually the whispers became louder. I was truly frightened by now and sweating profusely. What could have happened to her? Could this be a trap? Just as I was ready to leave, I heard a small voice: "Here I am."

I did not stop to ask questions, or even to kiss her in greeting. She climbed on behind me and we raced through the dark countryside until we crossed into the American sector. No one stopped us on the border, and only when we were across did we feel safe enough to talk to each other.

Over the next six months we lived hand-to-mouth, hiding out with sympathetic Germans for a while and then moving on. Here, in southern Germany, there was adequate food. This area had not been heavily damaged by the war. Despite the chaos in the country after the Nazi defeat, there was practically no lawlessness and we felt relatively safe. We were constantly helped by Virginia's flawless German.

As soon as we were all together, the three of us went to the American consulate in Stuttgart to ask for help avoiding deportation to Russia. The consul sympathized with our situation, but said he could not violate the Yalta agreement, no matter how tragic our situation was.

"The only thing I can do for you," he said, "is to say that I have never seen you." He suggested that we disperse ourselves in any way we could. In other words: Get lost. We did.

At the same time, the displaced Armenians in Germany were

beginning to get organized through the help of the United Nations Relief and Rehabilitation Agency (UNRRA), the American National Committee to Aid Homeless Armenians (ANCHA), and other supportive groups. The empty military base, *Funken Kazens*, in Stuttgart was opened to Armenian refugees. We felt relatively safe from forceful deportation there and began, very slightly, to relax from the terrible life-and-death struggle of the past five years. I also felt the stirrings of freedom for the first time in almost twenty years. I felt I could trust my fellow Armenians and we began to speak our minds.

The UNRRA was then providing food to many DPs from Eastern Europe and the Soviet Union. One of the UNRRA workers was an American woman who was delighted to hear that I was from Leningrad. She knew many scientists from Leningrad, she said. In fact, they were from my Institute. She explained that she owned an apartment building in New Jersey, near the RCA installation there. During the 1930s she had rented rooms to several Soviet electronics engineers who were being trained at the RCA laboratory for six months before being sent back to Leningrad.

"You should be proud of me," she continued, smiling brightly. "I'm a patriot, like you! The Soviet government asked me to put some listening devices in the rooms where the scientists were staying so they could spy on their private conversations. Of course I wanted to help, so I did. I wondered if they would be back again!"

How could I explain to her that, because of her eagerness to help the KGB, some of the brightest engineers in my department disappeared, either to the Gulag or perhaps even to death. No, I would not return to the Soviet Union.

We were all waiting for a chance to emigrate to any western country that would be willing to take us, but especially to the United States. While we were living in Stuttgart, we never stopped bombarding the American consulate with letters asking for emigration visas. In our petitions, we mentioned our education, our proficiency in various trades and technical fields, and our willingness to undertake any job, if only we could live in a free country.

None of us ever received a reply. It was frustrating and very discouraging. We knew that the UNRRA would end its operation sooner or later and we'd find ourselves living in a devastated Germany without having proper papers, without jobs or homes, once the *Funken Kazens* was closed. I spoke of my hopes of going to the United States to an Armenian-born American, George Mardikian. A San Francisco restaurateur, he had been sent to Europe by General Eisenhower to investigate how well GIs were eating. He encouraged me, but said he had to return to the U.S. to see what he could do for me.

Someone in Germany gave me the name of a Russian émigré now living in New York, a physician, Dr. Bogdasorov. I sent him desperate appeals for help, especially for an "affidavit of support," which was necessary before we could get a visa. He did respond, by sending an unsigned and therefore totally worthless affidavit. I became very angry with him, wondering why he even bothered to address an envelope to us.

I also had an opportunity to talk with Eleanor Roosevelt, widow of the American president. She was in Germany to help with relief efforts. I pled my case before her and asked her to help my family get to America. Her answer was no different: We must return to the Soviet Union, according to the Yalta agreement.

Frustrated as I was, I decided to visit the American consul once more. He spoke German well and we were able to converse freely in that language. He again expressed his sympathy about our desperate situation, and then said if we insisted, all he could do for us would be to give us a visa to the United States.

We weren't sure that we had heard him correctly. Then he added that it would be a disaster for us to go to the U.S., considering my age (38), my lack of English, and the fact that I didn't know a soul there. "You'd regret it all your life if you decide to go," he concluded.

Virginia and I sat for a moment, stunned. Then she realized that the consul had said we could have visas to the very country which from childhood was my Shangri-La. I could tell she was about to jump up in joy, but I was cautious and put out an arm to restrain her. I did not want to appear too eager to accept this wonderful offer.

I said to the consul, "We are grateful to you for your warnings to us about the perils we will surely face in the United States. And yes, we will probably regret that we did not heed your advice. On the other hand," I continued sorrowfully, "we will have to take this chance, because we have no alternative."

With an expression on his face as if he were giving poison to a man about to commit suicide, the consul gave us the necessary documents. We solemnly accepted them and slowly walked from his office into the corridor. There we saw a huge pile of unopened letters—hundreds and hundreds of them—all from DP's with applications for visas. I am sure my letter was also in that pile.

As soon as we were out of the building, Virginia and I began to show our relief and joy. We still had fears—the ease of the transaction seemed too good to be true—but hope began to bubble in our hearts. We couldn't wait to get on board the ship to America.

Three weeks later we had completed all the necessary paperwork. We were to travel under the auspices of the Church World Services, which would pay for our transportation on the promise that we would repay the debt as soon as we began earning money. Now we were on our way to Bremenhaven to board a ship bound for New York. Thus we became the first Armenian DPs to leave Europe, beginning a historic exodus. Over the next three years, 4,500 Armenians would follow us, most with the help of George Mardikian's ANCHA.

There were already several thousand DPs in Bremenhaven, newly liberated from various slave labor camps, all looking like we did—emaciated, ragged, dirty, unhealthy, and certainly unattractive. The women had not had their hair or skin cared for in years. The men, many unshaven, looked like panhandlers, despite the fact they were among the best educated men in Europe. Most children appeared more like little old people than children, with haunted eyes and unsmiling mouths. Many were suffering from nutritional deficiency diseases, and we were referred to as "pediculous"—lice infested. Again we were huddled together in makeshift barracks, but this time we were not waiting for starvation, torture, or death. Life had come back into our voices and eyes. Our wounds would heal.

At last we boarded the *U.S.S. Ernie Pyle*, a Liberty ship. But we still could not relax. Rumors suddenly spread throughout the ship that the previous ship leaving with Soviet DPs for New York had been inexplicably diverted to Leningrad instead.

The port authorities denied the report, unconvincingly so we thought. We decided not to take a chance. We would spend the first night on deck, watching all night. If we could see the lights of the English Channel, we were headed for America. If not, we were on our way back to the Soviet Union. Many of us vowed to jump overboard rather than return to Leningrad. The tension increased minute by minute.

Then, just at daybreak, we saw the lights of the English Channel. We shouted and cheered, jumped up and down and kissed each other. Karik watched us, bewildered. He had never seen us acting so wildly. All of his life we had been in hiding, whispering, trying to be invisible.

Unfortunately, some of the weakened and elderly passengers collapsed with the release of tension. Seven died of heart attacks. Their bodies were wrapped in canvas and thrown overboard after a short service. During the next eleven days of the journey, eight more people died of overeating. After so long a period of starvation, the great amount of food available on the ship was too much for them. They too were buried at sea.

On the eleventh day, we began to see the shoreline of America and then the skyscrapers of New York City. We moved into New York harbor up the Hudson River. Everything around us looked dazzling—clean, new, and prosperous, untouched by the long, devastating war in Europe. However, the Statue of Liberty looked much smaller than we had expected after our long dreams. But it did not matter now.

After one more night on board, during which we could hardly sleep, custom officials checked our documents, and then slowly we walked down the gangway to America and freedom. It was February 18, 1947. We were home!

With my rescuer from the Gestapo, in Berlin, years after the end of the War.

This is how I looked shortly after WWII in a DP camp, in Germany

On the way to Bremenhaven, Germany, for boarding the ship for America.

S.S. Ernie Pyle which brought me and my family to New York, February 18, 1947.

Greeting "The Lady with the Torch" on my arrival in New York.

FIVE

*A*ll the diverse elements of American culture that we would struggle with in our immediate future were in front of us as we disembarked from the *U.S.S. Ernie Pyle*. The Statue of Liberty that had for so long loomed so large in my mind as a symbol of freedom seemed disappointingly small. While skyscrapers in the distance glistened and shone, we were worrying about how we were going to overcome the many difficulties inevitable for most immigrants to the new world. We heard angry shouts in a language we could not understand and at the same time, we saw welcoming smiles from people inviting us to trust them.

In a long line we filed through the immigration stalls and numbly answered the questions asked of us. It was an unknown and confusing world, but it did not overshadow our happiness of finally being in America, although we could not speak English, had no money, and no friends or family. We had only each other.

Fortunately, someone was waiting for us—a woman from the World Church Service. Somehow she found us, put us in a taxi, and got us to our hotel at the corner of Broadway and 52th Street. Hundreds of motor cars sped along the Henry Hudson Parkway, nearly taking my breath away. Sirens screamed, horns blared, tires squealed. New York seemed to be the noisiest city I had ever heard, and certainly the most crowded.

Right away I could see that Americans were in a hurry. They cut across streets paying no attention to traffic lights. Drivers acted as if they hated to stop, pausing for red lights only when they had no choice. If someone slowed down for any reason, horns honked impatiently until traffic picked up again. The sound of horns echoing off the buildings stayed with me for hours, as well as the shouts of irritated drivers.

New York was very different from the European cities I knew or had read about. There seemed to have been no attempt at creating a beautiful city, or even an attractive one. It looked thrown together without a plan. After coming from a place where every piece of string was hoarded for future use, the mounds of trash here seemed extravagantly wasteful.

But we had no time for contemplating our first impressions. We got out of our taxi at a dreary old six-story building. That was to be our home for at least two months, because our sponsors had paid for our room in advance. This was a great relief to us. Then our guide handed me $50 and disappeared.

With apprehension we climbed to our room on the second floor. We had been able to bring very little with us—some clothes, shoes, a few books. Now we had to get on with the very serious business of building a new life.

But almost as soon as we settled in, I got sick. Our room seemed stifling, uncomfortably overheated. Although it was February and quite cold outside, the heat in the room was almost unbearable. We kept the windows open day and night. It was beyond our comprehension that Americans felt so free to waste fuel.

After a few days, when I didn't seem to be getting better, Virginia called the Russian-language newspaper, *Novoe Russkoye Slovo*, asking them to recommend a Russian or German-speaking doctor. At that time, doctors were not afraid to make house calls.

Soon someone knocked on the door. The man introduced himself in Russian. He was the very doctor who had sent us the worthless affidavit when I had so desperately pleaded for support. Some coincidence! He recognized my name and suddenly became quite frightened.

"How did you get here?" he asked. "Remember! I cannot support you!"

"Don't worry," I replied. "We know your affidavit was worthless. You do not have any responsibility toward us."

He was noticeably relieved, gave me medicine, and left.

A week later he returned and volunteered to show us the town. He took us by subway to the Bowery. Pointing to the derelicts lying on the street, he asked, "What do you see here?"

"A bunch of drunken people," I answered.

"No," he said contemptuously, "it's you—you are looking at yourself after two years in America. How could you dream of any future for yourself, coming to America at your age, with no money, without knowing a single word of English?!"

We were speechless. He continued, holding out a handful of bills, "Here! Take this money and go to the Soviet consulate. Tell them that you realized you made a great mistake coming to America, and now you want to go back to the Soviet Union."

Our indignation boiled over. "You take it, you dirty communist!" shouted Virginia and threw the money in his face. He scooped it up and ran from us as if we were going to kill him.

We stood watching him go, more disheartened than we had been in years. Without a word of English in our minds, we had to find a way home. We knew we couldn't figure out the subway system, so we started to walk. After two hours, we finally arrived at our hotel. We felt this was a test of our resolve not to be discouraged about life in America. But it was only the first of many.

We had to learn not only a new language, but new social customs, currency, laws and regulations, and ways of looking at life. For instance, residents of the Soviet Union are used to waiting in line patiently for hours. Americans will not do this for ordinary things, like food or household products because they are used to getting such things instantly, but they will wait in line to see a famous movie star. Americans are very trusting and sympathetic, yet they do not greet strangers on the street, only people they know. And they're always optimistic.

When two Americans meet, they ask each other, "How are things?" They always reply, "Fine!" They will say "Fine!" even if their mother died the day before. By contrast, when two Soviets meet and ask each other, "How are you?" They always say, "Normal," or "So-so." They will not tempt fate, especially if things are going well.

Soon after our visit to the Bowery, Virginia became concerned about our hotel. "Why is it so unusually quiet during the day," she asked me, "while late at night there is so much commotion? You'd think it would be the other way around."

We did some investigating and found out that this hotel, where we were sent by the World Council of Churches, was actually a "house of pleasure" catering to sailors! We decided to move out as soon as we had an opportunity.

We had been very frugal with our $50, eating only cereal, bread, and milk, and thus were able to survive until Virginia got a job as a cleaning woman. With her first income, we moved to a dilapidated apartment on 69th Street near the Third Avenue El. We got used to the shattering noise of the train day and night, but couldn't get used to the bedbugs or to the huge rats that roamed through the rooms at night. Sometimes they even came out during the day.

Still, we were very happy. At least we did not have to share this apartment with six other families, as we did in Leningrad. Virginia would say, "What else do we need? We already have hot running water!"

We enrolled Karik in P.S. 82 in our neighborhood. Like his parents, he did not speak English and his first year in school was not easy.

"He is so stupid," his teacher would tell us. "He doesn't understand my simplest questions."

We tried to explain that we were refugees from the Soviet Union and this was only our first year in this country. But our words were wasted on her. She could not comprehend why a ten-year-old boy could not understand her simple questions, particularly when she shouted them so loud. "Every child in America speaks English. Why doesn't your son?" she kept asking us. Her solution was to seat Karik in the back of the room and ignore him.

I told Karik that once the Russian author Gogol wrote to his mother from Florence. "Florence is a wonderful place. Even the children speak Italian here!" We laughed and tried even harder to learn this difficult language called English.

Three years later this "stupid" child was vindicated by becoming the valedictorian of his graduating class, a very proud moment for all of us.

Meanwhile, Virginia found another job making stuffed animals in an attic. No English was required. This was the type of sweatshop work that non-English speaking immigrants have always found and still do today. She began to make friends among the other DPs in the city. Virginia made friends easily and was loved by many people because they were able to trust her. She never broke a confidence.

We forced ourselves to speak only English at home, to listen to the radio, and to read English-language American newspapers. We tried to stop reading Russian-language American papers, thinking they would slow us down, but often we deviated from that self-imposed rule. I began taking English classes at night with other refugees. Our instructor was a Soviet sympathizer who referred frequently to "fascist America." Eventually we demanded the removal of this teacher and his indoctrination. After much study and practice with the other students, I was able to understand and read many words in English. Then I learned to speak a few key sentences.

I do not learn languages easily. I grew up with Armenian, attending an Armenian school. Because we lived in the Soviet Union, I also learned some Russian as a boy, but was not fluent in the language. I never learned more than a few words of Georgian. When I moved to Leningrad, I struggled with learning Russian for two years before I felt comfortable speaking it. In Germany, while we were hiding out from the manhunters, I learned what German I had to for survival. Now, in my middle age, I was trying to learn English. The grammar and syntax were alien to me. The vocabulary was easier to pick up, but language is not merely isolated words: "book," "car," "vegetable." I had to be able to put these words in context, to use verb tenses, appropriate adjectives and adverbs, make prepositional phrases, and most important, understand idioms.

Virginia and I were interviewed in a Russian-language newspaper about our new life in America as the first Soviet DPs from Germany. The article caught the eye of a White Russian, V. Radeev, who was manager of the drafting department of the Westinghouse facility in Jersey City, New Jersey, that manufactured electrical controls for elevators. He came to New York City to meet me. Afterward, he helped me secure a job as a junior draftsman in his plant and we became friends.

It was a much better job than I'd had before—I was then working as a manual laborer, cleaning stores and washing cars—and I was grateful for it, but it still was not in my field and I felt strongly that I wanted to utilize my energy and engineering background. There I merely copied plans for the wiring circuits for these controls and did not need to speak or understand much English. A young woman acted as my interpreter in case I needed help. She was Italian and spoke only a little Russian, but presumably her English was good enough to be understood. Radeev also acted as interpreter for me on many occasions.

Eventually someone in the organization thought I would be more valuable to the company working as a scientist in Westinghouse's research lab in Pittsburgh. When I told Virginia about the possibility of moving to Pittsburgh, she vigorously protested. She was just now adjusting to New York and did not feel she could endure another move. So we stayed.

Gradually we were able to buy some household goods, new clothes, and other material things that made life easier and more enjoyable. We wanted to be Americans and wearing American-made clothes helped us feel more like citizens and less like refugees. I even bought a car—a used 1941 Plymouth on installment payments. When I learned to drive, I felt like a king.

I was so proud of my Plymouth that I wanted to keep it looking good. This was not easy in New York City. Using my engineering aptitude, I devised a way to wash it almost nightly. I'd park the car by the curb, positioning it just under our kitchen window. Then I'd hook up a hose to the faucet, open the kitchen window, and spray the water on my car. Because we were on the second floor, occasionally a passerby was caught in the shower. Even though I made a practice of doing this only late at night when I thought no one was around, I received so many complaints, I had to abandon my scheme and leave my car to the mercy of the elements, like everyone else.

I know no one who has tried another language who hasn't gotten into trouble with idioms. Once when we were driving in downtown Manhattan, we went through a red light. A patrolman flagged us down and ordered us to the curb. He got out of his car, peered through the driver's side window of our car, and began to write a violation ticket.

We apologized for the error and tried to explain our dilemma. Hearing our terrible English, he changed his mind and said, "Forget it. It's on the house."

Virginia became very upset. "Officer," she said, "please do not put anything on my house. Please give us a ticket." Puzzled, the policeman started moving away from us. Virginia got out of the car and followed him, shouting, "Officer! Please give us a ticket! We want to have a ticket! Please!" The poor fellow ran away and Virginia returned to the car very disappointed.

I had trouble communicating with a German-speaking doctor, who I went to see about removing a small hemorrhoid, although the problem was not language. During the examination I suddenly felt a very sharp pain. I screamed out and pushed the doctor away, asking him what he was doing to me.

He replied very honestly, "You had such a small hemorrhoid that I couldn't charge you an adequate fee. Therefore, I had to make it bigger, so I could charge you enough."

I left, without paying a cent.

Sometime while we were still living in that dreary apartment on 69th Street, I was home sick one day with a bad cold. A visitor knocked on my door and I was amazed to meet Alexander Kerensky, the premier of the 1917 Provisional Government of Russia. He had gotten my address from someone and was eager to meet the very first post-war DP from the Soviet Union. Karik had just heard about him in his history class and was stunned to see him in our very apartment.

Kerensky, then in his late sixties, looked like someone's white-haired, kindly uncle, and indeed he acted that way toward Russian émigrés. He had left Paris for New York in 1940 as the Nazis arrived and had sounded warnings about Stalin, who he feared would become "the butcher for the whole world." He probably knew by then that he would never return to the Soviet Union, although occasionally he professed a hope that he would be able to restore some type of democratic government there.

When Kerensky visited me, his wife had just died after a long illness, he had sold his *dacha* in Connecticut, and he was fighting off a depression. The arrival of DPs gave him a new interest, which quickly became a passion. He decided to meet every Soviet DP who arrived in New York. Among them were many of his supporters who had been silenced by the Stalin regime.

Virginia's father, a Social Democrat, had been executed during Lenin's terror shortly after the Revolution. As a result, she was a very strong anti-Communist (her friends called her "Charlotte Corday"). When the first post-war Soviet dancers arrived in New York to perform in Madison Square Garden, Virginia picketed the performance with a sign reading "Stalin is the Enemy of the Russian People!" It gave her great satisfaction.

I had one short-lived foray into Russian-style politics after we'd been in New York for a while. Two leading Mensheviks from the pre-1917 Russian Social Democratic Labor Party, Abramovich and Nicolaevsky, now lived in the city. They claimed they were anti-Communist, so I agreed to attend one of their meetings. As soon as I entered the hall, I saw that it was decorated with the hammer and sickle of the Communist (or Bolshevik) Party. When I questioned the use of this symbol, I was told that it belonged to the Mensheviks before it was appropriated by the Bolsheviks. That was enough nonsense for me. I left and never attempted to contact them again.

Anti-Communism was a major factor in American life at that

time. In March 1946 former British prime minister Winston Churchill had visited the U.S. and made a speech in Fulton, Missouri, stating that "from Stettin in the Baltic to Trieste in the Adriatic, an iron curtain has descended across the Continent. Behind the line lie all the capitals of the ancient states of central and eastern Europe. Warsaw, Berlin, Prague, Vienna, Budapest, Belgrade, Bucharest, and Sofia, all these famous cities and the populations around them lie in the Soviet sphere and all are subject in one form or another, not only to Soviet influence but to a very high and increasing measure of control from Moscow."

Americans, with their hypervigilant sense of fair play, had judged it unfair that Soviet troops, their former allies, showed no indication that they would be leaving the nations they had liberated from the Germans—Poland, Czechoslovakia, Hungary, and Eastern Germany. They certainly were not going to pull back from the small countries they had absorbed during the war—Lithuania, Estonia, Latvia, and so forth. Americans began to get nervous. Where would the Soviets go next?

A joke that we heard about this time went, "Will there be a Third World War?" "No, but there will be such a fight for peace that it will nearly kill us."

A hopeful outcome of World War II was the formation of the United Nations organization. Its aim was to put an end to war by offering a forum for negotiation. After meeting first in San Francisco, the group chose New York City as its world headquarters. The most powerful nations made up the "big five" permanent members of the Security Council: the U.S., the U.K., France, China, and the U.S.S.R. This set the stage for an almost steady stream of confrontations between East and West in the years ahead.

We DPs did what we could to tell our stories about what life under Soviet rule was like. I myself did my share by publishing two articles in the Armenian literary magazine, *Armenian Review*. One article was "The Manhunt," the other was "The City of the Dead." For the first few years after the war, Americans sentimentalized DPs, especially those who had fled Communist rule, and the press was full of stories of their heroism in resisting Communism. President Harry S. Truman had signed the Displaced Persons Act in 1948, allowing for the immigration of 205,000 DPs. (As many as 12 million DPs were roaming Europe at that time.) Then, subtly, the mood changed and we were sometimes accused of being Bolsheviks and untrustworthy, even though we had risked our lives to escape Bolshevism. Within a year, where once the "golden door" had been open, the McCarran Act tried to close it by putting limits on immigration, particularly from Eastern Europe. The House Un-American Committee began its investigations, looking for Soviet sympathizers and "fellow travelers" among native-born Americans.

DPs were a little different from earlier immigrants. By and large, we were older, better educated, and more committed to freedom. We wanted to become Americans, but we also wanted to retain some of our culture—the literature, music, celebration of holidays, and religion, for instance. In New York, we were lucky, because there were already Orthodox churches, Russian delis, and a Russian-language newspaper. Many of our children wanted no ties with their past and Americanized their names.

There were many Russian émigrés in New York that we found an affinity with. Many were White Russians, who had left their country around 1917. Some were quite prominent, such as composer Sergei Rachmaninoff, maestro Serge Koussevitzky, helicopter inventor Igor Sikorsky, and writers Vladimir Nabokov and Ivan Bunin (who, incidentally, translated Longfellow's *Song of Hiawatha* into Russian).

Rachmaninoff's daughter, the Countess Volkonsky, lived on the East Side of Manhattan with her beautiful daughter Sophie. We frequently were guests of theirs, at lunch or dinner. Sophie's hobby was reglazing bathtubs and she did our tub. She married an American diplomat and accompanied him to Guatemala, where he was almost assassinated by local Communists. Next they went to Israel and then returned to the U.S., where they abruptly disappeared with their two children. We never found out what happened to them.

We became special friends with an elderly couple, the Eugene

Somoffs. He had been Rachmaninoff's life-long secretary. They had a primitive cottage (a *dacha*) in a Russian colony called Chouraevka, near Danbury, Connecticut. The cottage, which was named *Izbouchka*, had neither electricity nor running water, yet it was a charming place, stuffed with books and mementos. There were always interesting people in Chouraevka, writers, artists, intellectuals of all kinds. The colony had been established by devotees of playwright Anton Chekov and had become a center for émigré life, where endless discussions about literature, art, and life, could be heard day and night.

One of the old-timers there was Uncle Yura, a fisherman, who would treat us with his catch of the day. When Karik, following his advice, caught his first fish in the creek there, he was very distressed to see blood on it. "Bring the iodine!" he called. When he was told that iodine wouldn't help the fish, he threw it back in. He couldn't bring himself to kill anything.

Gradually we were introduced to the best of American food at Chouraevka—fresh corn (which was cooked in minutes, instead of hours, the way Russians cooked it), tomatoes off the vine, and the various berries which ripened all summer in Connecticut. The Somoffs took us on a tour of New England, which we found enchanting, and we learned much about the history of our new nation.

The American writers Henry Wadsworth Longfellow, Ralph Waldo Emerson, Nathaniel Hawthorne, Louisa May Alcott, Herman Melville, Walt Whitman, and Mark Twain (after he left Missouri) had all lived in New York or New England. But my favorite was still James Fenimore Cooper, whose *Leatherstocking Tales* about frontier life, Indians, and American pioneers fed my imagination while I was a boy. He was probably the one most responsible for my desire to come to America.

Therefore, one of my goals was to take a pilgrimage to Cooper's grave in Cooperstown 180 miles from New York City. We realized that this would not be an easy task. No one knew where the grave was. Only after spending an hour or more combing the cemetery did we locate it.

When we found the two large, flat tombstones with the inscriptions for James Fenimore Cooper and his wife, Susan, we sat on the grass next to them, feeling overwhelmed by the solemnity of the moment. After about fifteen minutes, we rose in silence, leaving the flowers we had brought. Virginia was in tears, and we both felt we had visited the grave of a very dear relative.

Russian DPs found a special angel in Alexandra Lvovna Tolstoy, daughter of the great novelist and humanitarian Leo Tolstoy. Once a countess and owner of a huge estate in Russia, she came to the U.S. in 1931 with little but her ability to work hard. In 1938 she was joined by Titiana Schaufuss, a friend from Moscow with formidable energy and executive skill who had been helping Russian refugees in Czechoslovakia. They were both concerned about Russians who were suffering under the Soviet dictatorship, and in 1939 they had organized the Tolstoy Foundation with headquarters in Manhattan to help Russian refugees reestablish themselves once they managed to get to America. Many prominent Russian émigrés and wealthy Americans contributed to the foundation.

Alexandra Tolstoy was a large, rosy-cheeked woman with abundant energy. Her hobbies included gathering mushrooms in the woods, fishing for perch, raising Belgian sheep dogs, taking long walks at night, and writing extensively about her father. Her best-known work was a large volume called *My Father*, describing his life and deeds.

Toward the end of 1940 Miss Tolstoy located a farm which she thought would be a perfect place for refugees to recover from their ordeal and make plans for their future. Called Reed Farm for a long-ago owner, it was located in Valley Cottage near Nyack, New York, on the Hudson River, about thirty miles from New York City. The owner, a devotee of the great author of *War and Peace* and *Anna Karenina*, sold the farm to his daughter for a symbolic one dollar. At once it became a haven for those fleeing Stalin's terror.

When we first visited the farm, we found it a peaceful place, surrounded by beautiful country. There were four cows, fifty pigs, thousands of chickens, and fields of vegetables ripening in the sun. A makeshift dormitory had been built for the DPs—there were more than 200 new arrivals each month then—and the kitchen was always in use. A camp was opened in the summer for the children of DPs. Karik was able to attend that first year that we were in America, a great help for Virginia and me, since we were then still working at odd jobs. While he was there, Karik participated in an intense course of gymnastics. A love of sports developed which never left him.

In July 1948 Oksana Kasenkina, a teacher employed by the Soviet delegation to the United Nations, sought political asylum through the Tolstoy Foundation. Once she was safe at Reed Farm, however, she was somehow abducted by the KGB (as the NKVD was now called), taken to the Soviet consulate on East 61st Street, and held under house arrest for several days. Crowds gathered outside the consulate and the press followed the story closely. Did she want to be free or not? Was she a spy? Finally, she jumped out a window from the third story. She was taken to Roosevelt Hospital with internal injuries and multiple fractures, but at least she was free.

Two other teachers escaped from Soviet control at the same time. Mikhail and Epena Samarin with their three children hid out in New York, moving around the émigré community until he was granted asylum by the U.S. government. We hid his children for a while. In his statement he said, "My wife and I desire voluntarily to renounce our Soviet Citizenship. We will not under any conditions return to Russia and certain death." Indeed, the 1947 Soviet criminal code state that a refusal by a citizen to return to the U.S.S.R. would be considered treason. It continued, "Persons who refuse to return to the U.S.S.R. shall be declared outlaws. . . . Outlawing shall entail . . . confiscation of all property of the convicted person [and] shooting him to death within 24 hours."

One of my closest friends in New York was Leo Cheker, a CPA, who frequently invited us to his summer home in Long Beach, New York. Cheker was an altruistic social-democrat, the type I call an "armchair liberal." He had left Russia with his parents when he was four, and still spoke Russian quite well. Although he had a very comfortable life in America, he argued for the virtues of the Soviet system.

Cheker and I often had heated discussions on the subject, which fortunately did not affect our close friendship. We simply thought the other was misguided. One day I said to him, "Why don't you visit the Soviet Union to see for yourself?"

He replied, "Why should I? I can find out everything I want to know by reading here, in New York City." But the idea stayed with him and finally he decided to go and see this "brave new world" for himself.

One of Cheker's New York friends had a brother, a high-ranking Communist Party official, who lived in Moscow. Cheker visited this man and received from him a letter for the brother who lived in New York City. Believing that the letter was safe from government scrutiny, the man had written of his life under Stalin's terror and his fear of being arrested and deported to the Gulag, despite his high position and his extreme care not to do anything "wrong."

I had warned Cheker not to leave anything written in his suitcase at the hotel. He ignored my advice and stuck the letter in his bag. The KGB (as the NKVD was now called) found it immediately. At the airport, just as Cheker was about to board his plane, he was asked if he had anything to declare.

"Nothing," he said, "I left all my belongings with friends in Moscow."

At that moment a KGB agent grabbed him and tore off his jacket. Pulling out the letter from the jacket's pocket, he said, "You are under arrest for trying to smuggle a letter from the Soviet Union."

He was arrested on the spot and watched in anguish as his airplane took off without him. Immediately he was put in jail and interrogated. But Cheker, still not realizing the danger of the situation, began shouting at his interrogator, demanding to be released. During the argument, Cheker slapped him. The interrogator was astonished—nothing like this had ever happened to him.

Cheker was finally allowed to call the American ambassador, who said that he was sorry, but he couldn't do anything because Cheker had violated Soviet law by taking the letter with him. The ambassador could only add his name to the list of other Americans who, for one reason or another, were detained in the Soviet Union. "When you are released," he continued, "call me back so I can delete your name from this list."

Cheker's interrogation continued for three more days, accompanied by several fist fights. This behavior was so unorthodox that the interrogator concluded that this man was out of his mind, especially after he demanded to be put in touch with the *New York Times*. He threatened to buy an entire page to advertise that the Soviets were "bandits," and to say that no American tourist should visit or spend a single penny in the Soviet Union.

Cheker's position was made even more precarious because—against my advice—he had insisted on wearing a Zionist pin in his lapel. After four days of confrontation, a higher Soviet official decided that they were definitely dealing with a crazy man and ordered Cheker's release. He left on the first plane out to Helsinki, Finland.

Cheker never realized that his complete ignorance of the gravity of the situation, as well as a mean right hook, saved him. After he returned home, I visited him in his New York apartment. He was still steaming with anger and agreed that the Soviet system was as bad as I had said.

Curiously enough, he still found something to praise in Soviet Russia. "Do you know," he said, "they are so smart! They take many historically interesting items and put them in a large house for display. They call these houses museums. Why don't we do the same thing in America?"

I was speechless for a moment, then I said, "Have you never noticed that we too have some 'large houses' in New York called museums?"

"No," he said with some surprise. "I guess I've been too busy making money."

We were very much a part of the Russian community in New York because Virginia could not speak Armenian. However, we occasionally made contact with the Armenians there as well. Soon after we arrived, we attended a gathering at the Waldorf Astoria Hotel which

George Mardikian, head of ANCHA (Armenian National Committee to aid Homeless Armenians), hosted. George introduced Karik to the crowd as the first Armenian DP in America and asked Karik if he could recite the Gettysburg Address, which he did rather well.

Much later I was recalling this event to another Armenian, William Saroyan, and referred to Karik's recitation of Lincoln's speech as the "Ginzburg Address." Saroyan laughed and commented that such a slip was probably due to the fact that I had too many students in New York named Ginzburg. (I was a teacher at this time.)

Now and then we attended the Cathedral of St. Illum-inator's Armenian Church on 27th Street and Second Avenue. We decided to have Karik baptized there. To his great embarrassment (he was ten years old), he had to stand in a basin of water before the congregation in his underwear, while the priest sprinkled him with holy water and anointed him with oil. The only thing that made it bearable for him was that none of his classmates was present.

As we became more sure of ourselves and could communicate with Americans fairly well, we began to enjoy the rich cultural life of New York City. Unlike Leo Cheker, we sought out the museums in the city—the Metropolitan Museum of Art, the Cloisters, the Museum of Modern Art, the Museum of Natural History, and so forth. Our meager income did not keep us from also attending the Metropolitan Opera or the New York City Ballet, which was then under the direction of George Balanchine, a native of my beloved Tiflis.

We walked through Central Park—in those days it was perfectly safe—and down Fifth Avenue, where we were thrilled with the elegance and imaginative displays. We never missed an Easter Parade, applauding the beautifully dressed women in their incredible, one-of-a-kind hats. Some had an entire garden on their heads. Some Sundays we enjoyed ourselves at Jones Beach, or we might go to LaGuardia Field, just to watch the airplanes take off and land.

Karik loved to listen to the radio. One day while he was listening to a quiz show, he decided to call in and respond. To our surprise—and his as well—he answered all the questions correctly and won. He was promised a prize. A few days later, a woman arrived with a huge Alaskan husky. She said, "Here's your prize!"

We stared at the monstrous dog. She continued, "It's yours now. Take good care of it and feed it no less than two pounds of the best beef you can get every day." The prospect of having this huge dog in our small apartment and feeding it with "at least two pound of the best beef" when we could not feed ourselves such beef horrified us. We refused to accept the gift and Karik was heartbroken, watching the dog leave. Ever afterward he was partial to large, hairy dogs and had one when years later he moved to California to go to college. Even now he owns a large Pyrenees.

During our first months in New York I wrote to Dr. Vladimir Zworykin, who was credited with the invention of the TV. He had visited my Institute in Leningrad about ten years earlier with his prototype of a television set. At that time he was a chief scientist with RCA Corp., and I hoped that he might be able to find a job for me in that huge organization.

His response was very discouraging. He remembered seeing me in Leningrad and said that he was happy I was now in America, but he did not see how I could succeed in this country at my age without being able to speak English. (By now I was very tired of hearing this everywhere I looked for work.) He suggested that I should get a job at the Lion Match Company in Queens, where practically everyone spoke Russian. It was owned by Dr. Boris A Bakhmeteff, a former hydraulic engineer and an early émigré from the Russian Revolution. It was almost a charitable organization, where Russians unable to learn English could find work at minimal wages. He also suggested that I forget about ever finding a job at RCA. I was too stunned to question his judgment.

Many years later, after I had authored and co-authored several scientific books and had become a "known quantity" in my profession, I decided to visit Dr. Zworykin and present him with a book I had recently published with several other scientists. He did not know the purpose of this visit and greeted me coolly. With a great sense of satisfaction, I plopped the book on his desk.

He was at a loss for words. Finally, almost reluctantly, he congratulated me, adding that he was very wrong for not giving me the opportunity with his company that I had sought. How much easier he could have made my struggle! Later I found out that the engineering staff engaged in the development of transistors at RCA was using this very book as a reference.

While I was still at Westinghouse, I applied to City College of New York to enroll in an electrical engineering class in order to familiarize myself with the English terminology in my field. My application was turned down because I did not have a high school diploma, which was a perquisite for all students applying to any college—no matter that I had the equivalent of a Ph.D. in the subject. As a DP, I had no documents. I was terribly disappointed, but they kept my curriculum vitae in their files.

Six months later, I received a letter from City College asking me to teach the same class I had tried to take. When I asked how this was possible, I was told that a high school diploma was not needed to teach courses, only to take them!

Bravely I started my new job. Bravery wasn't enough, however. The job was a nightmare for me as well as for my students. I mixed up German, Russian, and English terms. I was unable to understand the students' questions, which seemed to be fired at me with the speed of a machine gun. My class of thirty-two students shrank to eight. I was sure that was the end of my career at City College and was very surprised when the college extended my contract, first for the second semester, than for two more semesters.

The constant struggle to teach in English took its toll on my health. I developed a bleeding ulcer. On the advice of my doctor, I gave up teaching and started looking for a job in the industry.

Just at that time, a team of recruiters from General Electric Co., came to town. General Electric was then the largest single employer in New York State. Its main plant was in Schenectady, outside Albany on the Hudson River, where many scientists in a variety of engineering fields were employed. GE had just opened a new Electronics

Park in Syracuse. They were looking for electronics engineers to staff it.

In 1950 electronics was the largest growth industry in the country. That year more than seven million television sets were sold and it was predicted that the number would double the next year. Furthermore, the field was changing almost daily because of the introduction of a new element, the transistor. It promised to make the vacuum tube obsolete and revolutionize all the communications media, which it did. At that time, the largest companies involved in transistor development on the East Coast were Sylvania and Philco, besides GE.

After GE personnel interviewed me, they told me I should hear from them "soon." In two months (not very soon to me), I was invited to visit the electronics facilities at Syracuse for a final interview.

I was given most attentive treatment and taken through eight or nine departments so I could learn their operations. It was a field day for me! I had never seen such fascinating equipment and facilities. Everything was new for me. Everything was exciting. After being out of the field for more than ten years I had no idea of the progress that had been made. I felt like Rip Van Winkle.

Even more than the up-to-date equipment, I was impressed with the atmosphere in the lab. Dr. C. G. Suits was then the research chief at GE in Schenectady, and his attitude was evident in each of the company's seventeen labs: "Once hired, the men are turned loose in the lab and told to dive into whatever of the available projects they find most interesting." Such a philosophy had resulted in the development of thousands of profitable products and even in a Nobel Prize for one GE scientist, Dr. Irving Langmuir, who developed tungsten filaments and electron tubes, among a host of other inventions.

When I was asked which area I'd like to work in, I said I'd like to devote myself to a new technology where I thought I could contribute the most—transistors. I was introduced to the laboratory personnel engaged in transistor research and development and after another interview, I returned home.

My brain was buzzing with what I had heard and seen. I knew

I wanted to be a part of the lab team, but I did not feel sure that I'd get such an ideal job. A long two months passed without hearing a word. Then one day—the brightest in my life—I received a telegram informing me that General Electric was offering me the position of a development engineer in the transistor field.

It was not possible to express my joy and gratitude. This is why I had crossed an ocean not knowing anyone. This is why I had endured bedbugs and rats, why I had swept stores, why I had struggled to teach students the basics of electrical engineering in an alien language. All my dreams of America would come true, after all.

I immediately cabled GE that I was ready to start work at once. I wanted to put all of my energy into my new job and I believed I could succeed—despite the fact I was now forty-two and despite all the other handicaps that previous potential employers had told me I had.

Then I had a shock. Virginia did not share my enthusiasm. She was horrified by the prospect of leaving New York City, where she already had so many friends. Syracuse was a relatively small town, 300 miles away, and its Russian population then was probably very tiny, if it existed at all.

She was adamant and so was I. This time I could not permit her feelings to destroy my career. After so many years of living together and after enduring so many dreadful experiences together, we separated. I put my belongings in a car and drove to Syracuse, confident that I was doing the right thing for all of us.

The spectacular beauty of the drive across New York state confirmed my feelings. It was fall, and the colors of the changing leaves astonished me with their bright variety. The reds ranged from cinnamon to scarlet, the yellows from lemon to gold, and the counterpoint of deep green evergreens set off the scene. I had never seen such color in Europe, where the leaves turn from green to an undistinguished yellow to brown. When I saw my first New England fall, I was amazed and wanted to know more about this phenomenon. But as I drove to Syracuse I was content merely to enjoy the colors, reflecting for a moment on how death could be so beautiful.

I arrived in Syracuse on a Friday night. Not having a place to stay, I found the residence of the local Armenian priest, who was happy to give me shelter overnight.

That evening I told him that I had just accepted an engineering position at GE. However, my words did not register in his mind. He told me instead that he would try to get me a job as a coal deliveryman, explaining that it would probably be for the night shift and I should have my own wheelbarrow.

Patiently I tried to explain that I didn't need a job, I already *had* a job. But it was no use. He didn't believe me. I became so angry that in the morning I left his house and found a boarding house.

On Monday morning I was awake early. After eating what breakfast I could, I went to GE to start my new work. All of my premonitions were true. This was the start of my stimulating and all-absorbing professional career in America. I was extremely grateful for this opportunity and I did not disappoint my company.

SIX

*W*ith the same determination that had gotten me from Tiflis to New York, I began to make a new life for myself. I rented a two-bedroom apartment in Syracuse on the second floor of a new three-story building about twelve miles from the GE plant. It was a plain building, a very pedestrian 1950s style without landscaping, but to me the accommodations were deluxe, after living for four years in that run-down apartment in New York City.

My first few days at GE were somewhat confusing, although everyone did as much as they could to make me feel at home. I felt I had to put my engineering ability in high gear again, after so many years of keeping it in low. I joined a highly educated eight-man group of scientists and engineers from throughout the world: India, China, Switzerland, Canada, the U.S., and elsewhere. We were a small version of the U.N., with me representing Eastern Europe. We were called the "circuit group" (officially we were the Semi-Conductor Application Unit) and were given a spacious office and a secretary.

Our group was headed by Richard J. Shea, a graduate of MIT. The other members, besides me, were Charles A. Rosen, Woo Foung Chow, Sorab K. Ghandi, Vernon P. Mathis, Johannes S. Schaffner, and Jerome J. Suran.

After I'd been at GE for a few days, I was notified that a "delegation" of three people, including an Armenian priest, had arrived at the company, inquiring if a man named Edward Keonjian was an employee. They wanted to see me personally, to verify my association with

GE. They were ushered into my office and I introduced myself. They were more than a little surprised and perhaps even somewhat embarrassed to see that, indeed, I had told the truth and that my job was an important one.

I quickly got caught up in the intellectual excitement of working on a team which had a common goal. It seemed as if all my energy that had been tied up in merely trying to survive since 1941 was suddenly liberated. I felt like a boy again. The sense of shared discovery was exhilarating and our desire to work together far overshadowed any problems we might have had in trying to communicate with each other. We each spoke English, and of course the language of engineering is universal.

About six months after I moved to Syracuse Virginia decided to join me. I was relieved and delighted. I did not like being a bachelor and had been quite lonely. Karik had just graduated from public school as valedictorian and was eager to see his new high school. His English was excellent and he looked like any other American teenager at fourteen.

It took us a while to get used to Syracuse. Its population was only 200,000, and the pace of life seemed very slow. It was certainly quiet. There were none of the extras we were used to in New York City—magnificent libraries, museums, Broadway theaters, international exhibitions, and people from a variety of cultures. I don't know what history-minded Hellenophile named the town Syracuse, but he must have named the New York towns of Troy, Ithaca, and Utica, as well.

Syracuse's many Victorian-style homes stood on large lots shaded by huge trees. In the summer the gardens were lavish and inviting, with hollyhocks, sweet peas, roses, and calla lilies. Undistinguished newer apartments, such as ours, were going up around them as part of the postwar building boom. There was a blandness about Syracuse that was both comforting and irritating. Most of its residents were proud of its small-town feel and glad they did not live in a major metropolis. Perhaps because it was so different from anywhere else we had lived, we enjoyed finding our way around this new environment and making new friends. Before long Virginia found a job at Cross-Heinz Company, a large manufacturer of street traffic lights, working as a draftsman.

In the absence of an Orthodox Church, we visited a Presbyterian Church. We did not like the plainness of the sanctuary or the very matter-of-fact style of the service because we were used to the mystic awe inspired by Holy Communion. But we were truly horrified when the minister took off his robes to reveal a costume that he was wearing in some kind of a burlesque revue. It was all good-natured fun for the congregation, who obviously was not used to reverence in church, but it did not suit us at all. We did not return.

At last I was able to indulge my passion for travel. We branched out from Syracuse in our explorations of New York state and visited all the landmarks we could, beginning with Niagara Falls. We gaped at this marvel, where 200,000 cubic feet of water races over the lip (it doesn't merely *fall*) every single second, and then took the *Maid of the Mist* under the falls, getting thoroughly soaked, despite our oilskins.

New York State has a rich history that has never failed to interest me. So many ideas were born there that led to social changes in the entire nation. Joseph Smith had his vision of the angel Moroni in Palmyra and found the gold plates there that became the Book of Mormon; Susan B. Anthony proclaimed her movement voting rights for women at Seneca Falls; John Humphry Noyes advocated "group marriage" and communal child-rearing at Oneida; Ann Lee established a colony of celibate Shakers at Watervliet; and the escaped slave Harriet Tubman brought other slaves on the Underground Railroad through New York to freedom in Canada.

I often felt the spirit of James Fenimore Cooper around me as we traveled. His stories grew out of his life in the woods of upstate New York and from the tales he heard about the Iroquois Confederacy. That group, made up of Mohawk, Seneca, Onondaga, Onedia, and Cayuga tribes, had a very sophisticated political system and a long history of showing incredible courage under torture. They did not flinch in the face of death. I admired that bravery very much.

The Jesuits tried to Christianize these Indians in the late seventeenth century, but they did not respond well. Their own religion relied heavily on dream interpretation and a strong sense of community—they lived communally in "long houses" and each was responsible for the whole. They cooked together, sharing their resources; they supervised each other's children; and everyone took care of the sick and elderly.

Washington Irving's stories, too, inspired my imagination. When we drove east of Albany on one of our frequent trips to New York City, I could almost see his portly, red-faced Dutch merchants in their silk knickerbockers, puffing on their clay pipes. The Hudson River Valley was full of history, both legendary and actual. For instance, Robert Fulton tried out his first steamboat, the *Clermont*, on the Hudson. In the heyday of the steamboat, races were frequently held from Albany to New York City.

Thomas Cole was one of the few artists able to show the beauty of this valley, and his romantic landscapes changed the way American felt about their country. At first, they saw only land to be subdued and planted, but Cole and other artists of the so-called Hudson River School in the nineteenth century, convinced Americans that nature could be appreciated and enjoyed just as it was, without a plow.

On one trip toward New York City on Highway 9, we craned our necks to see Hyde Park, home of Franklin Roosevelt, then went by West Point, which had produced so many great American generals, including Robert E. Lee, Ulysses S. Grant, John J. Pershing, Dwight D. Eisenhower, and Douglas MacArthur. The next landmark was Ossining, where the notorious Sing Sing Prison was located.

On other side trips, we visited New York's wine country, where Niagara, Catawba, and a dozen other varieties of grapes grow, and explored the mountains through their nature trails—the inviting Catskills and the rugged Adirondacks. We went to Rochester to see the profusion of lilacs in May and to the Finger Lakes during the summer.

At a Saratoga Springs Arts Festival I met the great choreographer George Balanchine, who was also from Tiflis, as I mentioned earlier. He told me (in Russian) that his brother still lived in Soviet Georgia. He had not seen him for many years and decided at one time to take a chance and visit the Soviet Union. He met his brother at the Tbilisi (formerly Tiflis) airport, but immediately turned back to the plane—he was so afraid of being arrested by the KGB that he couldn't stay even an hour.

The wooded hills of the Saratoga battlefield were the site of a major victory for the Continental Army in 1777. That victory gave the Americans control of the Hudson River and Lake Champlain above it. (However, nearby Fort Edward was the scene of an American defeat.) Guarding the route to Lake Champlain during the War for Independence was Fort Ticonderoga, which has been reconstructed with its stone walls, canon, and battlement. When we visited the fort and saw the guides in their Revolutionary War uniforms, we felt a special tie with this historic place.

Whitehall, on the southern tip of Lake Champlain, has been called the birthplace of the U.S. Navy. In 1776 the shipyard there built a fleet of small, lightly armed vessels that held off the superior British fleet for a year, giving the Americans time to build their forces at Fort Ticonderoga. Lake Champlain itself is enormous, 107 miles long, and marks the border between New York and Vermont. It was also the site of a battle during the War of 1812 in which the Americans were again victorious.

In Syracuse, we celebrated our first Thanksgiving in a very unusual way. GE had arranged for the local TV station to film our Thanksgiving dinner to show how new citizens, from a communist regime, gave thanks on this uniquely American holiday. They were supposed to supply a turkey. An entire TV production crew descended on our small apartment. The heavy equipment they brought with them immediately burned out all the electrical fuses in the apartment.

An emergency generator was installed, which made a bigger mess. Then, a turkey was put on our table, which had been nicely set for the three of us. Just before filming began, we found out that the "turkey" was made of plastic. Virginia felt this was an insult and demanded to have a real bird. A member of the TV crew was dispatched to a local restaurant to fetch a well-cooked turkey with all the trimmings.

At last we were ready to begin. We were very nervous, especially Karik, who could hardly wait until the "dinner" was over. He managed to stay on camera all of seventeen seconds. I had prepared a script describing our blessings, which I read stiffly, with considerable difficulty. I had tried to memorize parts of it, but as soon as the floodlights were turned on, all words left my mind. Clips of Virginia shopping and me working in my lab were shown with my voice-over.

When the filming was finished, the crew began to pack up—and to pack up our turkey as well. This was too much for us. After making a mess in our apartment and of our holiday, we felt that we were entitled to keep the bird for ourselves. We expressed ourselves so forcefully that the crew had no choice but to leave it. Only after they left could we finally begin to enjoy our Thanksgiving dinner, giving thanks for our blessings.

The first Thanksgiving, it is said, was celebrated by the Pilgrims because they had survived disease, cold, famine, the wilderness, loneliness, and fear during their very difficult first year in America, when so many of their small company died. We Keonjians were also grateful beyond measure for having survived many similar ordeals. Some of the Pilgrims (and Puritans, Shakers, and Quakers) had even been imprisoned in England, and that experience must have strengthened their resolve to find freedom in the New World, as it did ours.

The legend says that four wild turkeys were caught and cooked for the first Thanksgiving dinner, the reason we still eat turkey at that meal. Those four turkeys could be symbols of the four freedoms I enumerated in my short talk on television: freedom of speech, freedom of religion, freedom of assembly, and freedom of the press. I also pointed out that I had been free to accept the job of my choice, something unheard of in the Soviet Union.

A week later the film was broadcast. I was out of town on business and asked Virginia to watch it and tell me how it looked. I returned home the next day and was impatient to hear her impression of the show.

"I didn't watch it," Virginia told me.

"Why not?" I shouted.

"Because I was too nervous," she said. "Also I didn't want to make you nervous by watching you on the screen."

I was very disappointed. Eventually the TV station sent us a copy of the film and I watched "The Keonjians at Home on Thanksgiving." Karik was very interested in it and even Virginia finally forced herself to watch it.

The next year Karik had another reason to be excited. One evening we were watching the 1953 Miss America Pageant on TV. The winner was Neva Jane Langley, a green-eyed brunette from Georgia—not my Georgia, of course, but the U.S.'s. My son instantly fell in love. He began dreaming about her all the time. One day I asked him if he'd like to see Miss America in person in our home. He laughed and said it could never happen.

Virginia replied, "Don't be too sure! Knowing your father, he just might bring her here. If he says he'll do it, he'll do it."

I was a member of the Kiwanis Club then. I suggested to them that we invite Miss America to Syracuse to give us a pep talk. They agreed and I wrote her a letter on Kiwanis stationery, telling her how much the club would be honored if she could speak to our meeting. I also mentioned that if she could come, she should stop at my house first and I'd take her to the meeting.

The invitation was accepted and we forgot all about it. Then one morning my son came running to me very excited, shouting, "Miss America is at the door! She's looking for you, Dad." After that, my son never doubted that I would do what I said I would do.

Besides the Kiwanis Club, I also joined Toastmasters International, to improve my English, and the Optimist Club. One of the fund-raising events for the Optimists was an annual "shoe-shining." We offered to shine shoes for a donation which we used to send underprivileged children to summer camp. We all had a good time doing this, and I found the event especially amusing. The Soviet Union had such a rigid class structure that something like this could never occur there.

Professional people simply would never shine someone's shoes, no matter the reason, and would certainly never laugh if they saw someone else doing it.

Most of the large corporations in America were expanding throughout the 1950s. Raw materials, energy, and labor were all relatively cheap and the consumer market was enormous, as more Americans moved into the middle class. It was often called the "Push-Button Age" because labor-saving devices, gadgets, and gizmos proliferated. The field of engineering was at the peak of its prestige. Slogans such as "More and Better Things for More People," "Live Better Electrically" and "Progress, Our Most Important Product" reinforced the idea that technology would make our lives easier and more fun.

Corporate money flowed into product research in abundance. At GE our labs were beautifully equipped and the library was stocked with up-to-the-minute periodicals and reports. The attitude in the early 1950s was a generous one: we shared information freely—within our group, within our company, and among engineers in general. I found the lack of secrecy wonderful because secrecy and distrust were so prevalent in Soviet Russia, and I never stopped being grateful for the freedom to experiment as I wanted.

Periodically, some of us were invited to attend the company's engineering brainstorming sessions. Our instructor would write a specific problem on the board and then ask each of us to come up with a solution, no matter how "out of the ordinary" our solution seemed. Then we'd discuss the feasibility of each proposed solution thoroughly, eliminating those which did not seem practical. The suggestions that were left would be discussed further at the next session. These sessions were always stimulating and we loved them. Engineers are happiest when they can successfully solve problems.

At one of these sessions, someone asked, "Why does GE make such good refrigerators?" In a burst of enthusiasm I replied, "To provide good products for Americans!"

There was a moment of silence followed by laughter. "No, Edward," someone said. "I'm afraid you heard too much about the 'good of the state' in the Soviet Union. In America, there's only one reason to make good products: to make good money!"

That was my introduction to American economic theory.

My task in our group involved development of temperature stabilization of various transistor circuits, especially amplifiers and oscillators. I had to design an arrangement which would permit the circuit parameters to remain stable in extremes of temperature. I filled up reams of paper with my notes. If the arrangement would work, I was elated. If not, it was "back to the drawing board."

It was very interesting to visit other companies engaged in transistor development. My visits to Bell Telephone Laboratories in New Jersey were especially stimulating. The Bell Labs carried out very advanced work in many fields, including transistors. They had the best equipment and an outstanding team of scientists. Among them was Dr. William Shockley, who together with his associates, Dr. John Bardeen and Dr. Walter H. Brattain, was awarded a Nobel Prize in physics in 1956 for work with semiconductors. This effort led to the invention of the transistor.

The spirited leader of development at the Bell Labs was its vice-president, Jack A. Morton, who inspired me to edit a book on microelectronics, the first in the field. He wrote the foreword for the book, which was published in 1963 by McGraw-Hill. Some of the contributors for that volume were also employed by the Bell Labs.

One of my concerns at GE was the electrical noise in transistors. In fact, I published several works on the subject in professional periodicals. I met an engineer at the Bell Labs who had devoted almost his entire career to investigating the problem of noise in a variety of electrical contacts. His immense experience in that field was especially valuable to my work.

At GE, our team worked with such diligence and enthusiasm that in less than two years we had accumulated a wealth of information and knowledge about "Mr. Transistor." Nine of us decided to put all our findings into a single book. Shea acted as editor, and we all worked on the manuscript, offering information from our particular field of expertise. What could have been a very chaotic situation moved very smoothly, in part because each of us was methodical and well-organized with our research. We also were eager to be the first to come out with such a book.

The book was published by John Wiley & Sons in 1953 with the title *Principles of Transistor Circuits*. It was the first book in this field and was an instant success. Translated into several foreign languages, it made us, the co-authors, instant celebrities among scientists and even among some sectors of the general public. The staid *Philosophical Journal of London*, among many other professional periodicals, gave it a rave review.

A few of us engineers who lived in the same general area formed a car pool. One morning someone brought up the subject of World War II. He had been a pilot on the "Flying Fortress." He described how he had narrowly escaped being shot during one of his raids on a German submarine in Keel Harbor. He succeeded in hitting the ship, however, which was partially damaged.

Another of the engineers spoke up. He had been a commander of a German submarine during World War II. "Do you remember the date of that attack?" he asked.

"Of course," the former pilot replied, and mentioned a date in 1943.

"Then it must have been my ship that you hit!" said the German. "We were the only one in Keel Harbor on that day."

We did not speak for the rest of the ride. This strange coincidence returned us to our own deep memories of that war and how we had survived it. How ironic that former enemies were now working together under the same roof at GE! We had wasted so much of our resources trying to kill each other. Because of our experiences, we abhorred war and now wanted to work for peace. We felt we were helping to maintain as peaceful a coexistence as possible with the Soviet Union, which was then the greatest threat to stability in the world. A "cold" war is always preferable to a "hot" one.

There was a hot war going on at that time in Korea, although it was called a "police action." At the end of World War II, Korea had been divided at the 38th parallel. North Korea was Communist, controlled by the Soviet Union, and South Korea was occupied by U.S. troops. In June 1950 North Korean Communists invaded South Korea. The United Nations authorized member nations to aid that nation, and President Truman named General Douglas MacArthur, then in charge of the occupying forces in Japan, as commander of the U. N. forces there. We were all nervous about China's reaction to the conflict and about the threat of one of the powers using another A-bomb.

I very much admired MacArthur. He was a strong general, a strong man who kept his word, and I didn't think he would blink in this very dangerous game of "chicken" that the Communists were playing. Therefore I was shocked and appalled when Truman fired him in the spring of 1951 because the general had called for pursuit of the North Koreans beyond the 38th N parallel. Truman thought MacArthur was insubordinate; I thought he was courageous and I took his dismissal almost personally. MacArthur believed he had to push the North Koreans, and the Chinese who had joined them, back beyond the 38th parallel to complete his mission of containing Communism.

I never forgave Truman for his poor treatment of this American hero (or American Caesar as his biographer called him), and many years later I befriended his widow Jean in New York City. In fact, I was privileged to escort her to West Point for a commemoration service held at MacArthur's statue.

Meanwhile, all three of us Keonjians were studying U.S. history and especially the Constitution in preparation for citizenship. We quizzed each other on important events, such as the American Revolution and the Civil War, and about the lives of the presidents. We had learned our lessons well, for in December 1952, five and a half years after we had landed in America, we became U.S. citizens. I regretted that I missed voting in the 1952 presidential election by only one month. I felt that Dwight Eisenhower, because of his experience as the commander-in-chief of the Allied during World War II, would make a good president. Millions of other Americans did too.

We felt secure in our new country, and our future was the brightest it had ever been. At that time our son legally changed his name to Edward, Jr., because his original name, Karen, was a girl's name in America. When he started receiving letters to "Miss Karen Keonjian," he decided it was time to change. However, we continued to call him by his nickname, Karik.

On March 5, 1953, a bulletin was flashed around the world that Josef Stalin was dead. He had suffered a massive brain hemorrhage, just as Franklin Roosevelt had, and never regained consciousness. The year after Stalin died, I was able to vote for the first time in an American election. It was a very proud moment for me, and since then I have never failed to cast my ballot in every election that I could, from school board to presidential.

Soon after becoming U.S. citizens, we applied for passports. Now we felt safe enough to travel abroad. Our first venture outside the country was to Canada. About a half-mile from the border, Virginia got the passports ready and, gripping them tightly in her hand, held her arm out the car window in preparation for showing them to the guard. How disappointed she was when he didn't even look! He merely waved us on.

"He must have been drunk," she declared. "How could he let us go through without even seeing our passports?"

Approaching Montreal, as we were going downhill, we suddenly felt that the car had lost its brakes. In a panic Virginia opened her window and shouted, "We have no brakes! Get out of the way!"

No one paid any attention. Fortunately we arrived safely in town, where the car was repaired and we were able to continue our sightseeing.

Our trip to Montreal and Quebec City was just the first of many out of the country. I loved being a tourist and seeing my boyhood dreams of travel come true. Over the next few years Virginia and I toured Europe on our vacations, now almost completely rebuilt after the war, and recalled that only specially selected Soviet citizens were permitted to travel abroad and only when their family members were left as hostages in the Soviet Union. These relatives were frequently held hostage so travelers wouldn't be tempted to defect. The Soviets citizens who were allowed to travel were frequently assigned some spying functions for their government. As Americans we were free to go anywhere and to stay as long as we wanted. It was just unbelievable to us.

In 1955 Karik graduated from high school and applied for enrollment at a very unusual private college in eastern California called Deep Springs, a fully accredited liberal arts school. It was located on a remote cattle ranch in the Inyo-White Mountain range, nearly equidistant from Reno and Los Angeles, and the total enrollment did not exceed twenty-five students, all young men. Karik was one of the five candidates admitted that year. It offered a full room, board and tuition scholarship. It was a most unusual gift for both of us and again I told myself and whomever would listen, "only in America."

The curriculum of this three-year college was unique. Not only was it academically demanding, it also required the hard work of operating a cattle ranch. (It has been referred to recently as an "academic boot camp.") The philosophy and setting had been chosen by L. L. Nunn in 1917. He described the purpose of the school as offering education which emphasized "the need and opportunity for unselfish service in uplifting mankind from materialism to idealism, to a life in harmony with the Creator." It also prepared students to face anything that came their way, including graduate and professional schools. Karik became so taken with the West that after graduation he attended other universities in the West. Eventually he received a law degree from the University of Arizona. He never returned to the East for longer than a few days each year during the next forty years of his life.

After Karik's first visit home in the summer of 1956, we decided to drive him back to California, which would give us a chance to see some of the National Parks. We took our new Oldsmobile. It turned out to be a complete lemon, forcing us to stop for repairs many times on the trip. We did not mind, however. It gave us more of a chance to see the country. On the way home, Virginia and I stopped at several other national parks, which we had missed before.

Photography had always been a hobby of mine, although understandably I hadn't been able to indulge it in Leningrad during the Russo-Finnish War or during World War II. Now I took my heavy, old Rollieflex double-lens camera and Zeiss Contax-III everywhere I went. On this cross-country trip I took hundreds of photographs, as I would on future travels. Occasionally I won awards for my pictures. I always composed my shots carefully, but it was often the unexpected—a sudden shaft of light or a momentary shadow, a certain look in someone's eye or an engaging smile—that won the awards. I had no control over these things, but I managed to be there, at the right time, with my camera ready.

After two years at GE, the company decided to send me to Chicago to deliver a talk at the National Electronics Conference. I was still struggling with English and the thought made me very nervous. I had never spoken to an American audience, but I was told that the only way to learn public speaking is to do it. So I went. With shaking knees I stood up before 800 engineers, speaking as clearly as I could. Afterward I asked some of my associates from Syracuse, "How was I?"

"Not too bad," one said.

To me, that meant "good" and I was very proud of myself. Only much later did I realize that "not too bad" also meant "not too good."

My poor English was still getting me in trouble. One day I was telling my colleagues about life in the German forced labor camp. I explained that returning to the barracks from the factory one evening I found a dead pheasant in the woods. It was still warm and had probably just been shot by a poacher. (It was illegal to kill wildlife.) I picked it up and brought it to the barracks, where Virginia was able to secretly cook it on the wood stove. By being very careful not to let anyone one else know about the bird, it provided us with extra nourishment for three or four days.

While I was telling this story, I mistakenly used the word "peasant" instead of "pheasant." Soon afterward, I noticed that my colleagues began avoiding me. After a while, I demanded to know why and learned that they considered me a cannibal. It took a great deal of explaining to convince them otherwise.

Once while I was in Chicago on a business trip, I was relaxing in a bar. Sitting next to me was a short middle-aged man. We talked for almost an hour about my work and life. He mentioned that he was in the newspaper business. Then he asked if I'd ever really seen Chicago. I said no, just the airport and hotels.

"In that case," he said, "I'd like to show you around." He suggested we start our tour immediately. It was then after midnight.

At first I was hesitant to accept his offer, because I'd heard so much about Chicago gangsters and didn't want to end up wearing a "cement overcoat." But my companion looked trustworthy, so I followed him to his expensive car to see Chicago by night. During the two and a half hours of our tour he pointed out many prominent buildings in and around the Loop, telling me historical tidbits about each—the Water Tower, the Tribune tower, the Field Museum, Art Institute, and so forth. His knowledge was extensive and he turned out to be the perfect guide.

Around 2:30 a.m. he dropped me off at my hotel, handing me his business card and inviting me to call him the next time I was in town. As I was getting out of the car, he called me back.

"What will you bring your wife from Chicago?" he asked.

"I don't know," I answered.

"How about a pair of gloves? I suggest you try Marshall Field's department store. It's the best store in town."

The next day I went to the store and told the clerk in the glove department that it had been recommended by a man I'd met in a bar. I handed her his card, not even looking at it myself. She was very surprised. Instead of showing me some gloves, she called the manager and gave him the business card.

The manager turned to me with a big smile. "Let me pick out some gloves for you," he said cordially. He selected not one pair, but four pairs of the best stock. When I got out my wallet to pay, he said, "This is on the house."

By now I was familiar with the expression and was very happy to hear it, but quite puzzled. Why should they give me such a gift? I took the business card back and looked at it. The name read: Marshall Field III. Indeed, the publisher of the *Sun-Times* and director of Field Enterprises did know a thing or two about Chicago.

I was progressing very fast in my work and having a lot of fun doing it. I was thinking, even then, about alternate forms of energy and came up with the world's first solar-powered portable radio transmitter in 1954, which I built with the assistance of my technician, James O'Hern. It was the size of a pack of cigarettes and its principal advantage was that it used transistors instead of tubes and selenium energy converters instead of batteries. There was no need to replace batteries and it was extremely lightweight. Sunlight striking the selenium generated enough electrical energy to operate the transmitter, which, unfortunately, had a range of only 100 feet.

The range could have been improved by using silicon or germanium semiconductors instead of selenium, but still this solar-powered transmitter was very much ahead of its time. The cost of manufacturing such a device was too high to justify its production. The only place solar power received recognition then was in a science comic book. Maybe some young would-be scientists read that book, for the idea of solar power did not disappear. Five years later, with the beginning of space exploration, solar powered elements became practical and today are the only source of energy for space vehicles. As to my solar radio transmitter, it was prominently displayed in 1986 at the Museum of American History at the Smithsonian Institution in Washington, D.C., along with many other "firsts" in technology.

For other inventions our team was granted nineteen patents over the course of the next four years, nine were for me alone. However, there was no financial reward for me from any of them, since they were all assigned to GE. One patent was for an invention of constant voltage source for electronic circuits which would not change its value with variations of temperature. This concept is used today in all electronic circuitry worldwide.

I was especially proud of another of my designs, that for a micropower audio amplifier, which could operate continuously for three years. This was the smallest and most compact, practical amplifier up to that time which did not need an "on" or "off" switch.

Feeling much more confident as a speaker by now, I was giving presentations at various local and national engineering symposia several times a year. I published articles in professional magazines regularly, thirty-two in six years. In June of 1954 I joined the Scientific Research Society of America, a distinguished honorary society.

Once GE sent me to address a meeting of the national Secretaries Association in Washington, D.C. I felt that I had to break the ice, because the women looked very serious, as if they were expecting a scholarly talk. I told them that I thought women were strange creatures and I did not understand them.

"For example," I said, "when I told my wife I'd be spending the evening with four hundred women, she said 'That's nice. Have a good time.' But if I told her that I would be with two women, or one woman, do you think her reaction would be the same? I doubt it."

Smiles appeared and the ice was broken.

Because of the great success of *The Principles of Transistors*—several hundred thousand copies were sold world-wide—our team decided to publish a second book in the same field. That was a mistake. Only a few thousand copies sold and it did not receive the attention in professional journals that the first one did. Perhaps it was because of the composition of our group had changed or because there were so many books available on transistors and ours was just one more. After putting so much work into the project, its failure was very disappointing and we all lost interest in trying to publish another group effort.

Once I tried to pull a trick that almost backfired. To demonstrate to higher management the unusual capabilities of transistors, I bought a rubber monkey and attached nearly invisible wires to its arms and legs. Those were extended to the next room, where another engineer sat. It was his job to pull the wires on cue so "Chip the Monkey" would seem to respond to our commands.

The brass came in for their demonstration and I said, "Chip, raise your right arm" and "Chip, lift your left leg." He did. The observers were so impressed with our "transistorized" monkey, they wanted us to demonstrate it at the next stockholders meeting. We quickly disclosed the joke, but this did not dissuade them. They continued to insist that Chip perform for the stockholders. I guess they were too embarrassed to admit that they had been fooled. But wisdom prevailed, and Chip stayed in his cage.

Around that time we were visited by a vendor who brought a "talking voltmeter" to our lab. The numbers on the scale were transmitted by a female voice from an audio tape inside the voltmeter. For instance, if the voltmeter showed 74.00 volts, the recording would announce, "seven, four" and then in a very sexy voice give us the remaining zeros as "oooh! ooooh!" We thought it was hilarious.

One day while I was having lunch in the management section of the plant cafeteria, a middle-aged man asked me if I was Edward Keonjian. He then introduced himself as the director of personnel at GE and said that he'd been following my progress with the company.

Then with a broad smile he added, "when you applied for employment here, I said 'Over my dead body!' I wasn't about to permit a Bolshevik from the Soviet Union to step a foot into our plant. Now I'm so glad to see that I was so wrong about you. Please forgive me."

That was easy to do because I hadn't even known about it. He shook my hand and left. I didn't see him again. He must have been pretty naive. A new emigrant to America would never be recruited to spy. We were much too patriotic—and no one hated Communists as much as we did.

Bolshevik, Communist, un-American, and anti-American were all dirty words in the mid-1950s. Everyone wanted to promote patriotism. In 1955 Virginia's company sponsored a contest for the best essay on "What America Means to Me." She entered and won over one hundred other applicants. Our Congressman, R. Walter Riehlman, introduced the essay into the Congressional Record on July 28, 1955. Virginia had written:

"Upon looking back in my life in Communist Russia, I ask myself, "What was I?" A government-owned slave who could be put in jail for a day's absence from work. It was in America that for the first time in my life I felt like an individual, a person, a human being, not just a number. . . .

"My mind is not controlled by anybody. I can read and study whatever I wish, according to my personal inclination. . . .

"Many other things which some people born here take for granted are of greatest value to me. They are best summed up by the wonderful word *freedom*—the most precious of all my possessions today."

The Russian Center at the University of Syracuse offered a crash course in the Russian language sponsored by the U.S. Air Force. It was supposed to prepare English-Russian interpreters. Virginia spent three months trying to teach there and gave up because her English was not good enough. We met several graduates of the program and thought that with practice they could be fairly effective. Later we were dismayed to learn that their knowledge of Russian was wasted. They were never used as interpreters.

Twice I presented a talk on engineering education behind the Iron Curtain, comparing it with that in the United States. One was on October 22, 1954, at the ninth annual meeting of the American Society of Engineering Education (ASEE). The text of that talk subsequently appeared in the society's magazine the same year. The other was on March 9, 1957 at Ohio State University in Columbus.

I indicated that, despite all the shortcomings in the Soviet system, Soviet schools gave very good basic education. Soviet students didn't have to spend their first year in college catching up; they were well prepared. There were no electives in Soviet education and no "liberal arts" offering a broad cultural education. Instead there was a very rigid curriculum that included compulsory courses on the history of communism: the fundamentals of Marxism and Leninism; political economics and economic politics; dialectical materialism; and the history of the Communist Party. How many students pay attention during this indoctrination is unknown, but it is certain that they don't dare shut their eyes!

Soviet students pay no tuition and usually use library books for texts. They have to repay this free education after graduation by accepting assignments to work in various parts of the U.S.S.R. at a salary which the government determines. There are no choices.

The fundamental difference between Soviet education and that in Western countries is the same difference in all other aspects of life. The Soviets emphasize the importance of the state at the expense of the individual; the West emphasizes the importance of the individual as a member of a state. I ended my talk by saying, "The Soviet system completely destroys a student's most precious birthright, which is his personal freedom, and for which there is no substitute."

All of us refugees from Eastern Europe were grateful for freedom and were saddened and angered to watch the Soviet Union tighten its hold on its satellites. In the summer of 1956 both East Germany and Poland struggled to gain a little more freedom. At the end of October of that year, Hungarian students got permission to express sympathy with the Poles by gathering silently in front of Budapest's Polish embassy.

The group, carrying red, white, and green Hungarian flags, seemed peaceful. They marched to Petofi Square and then someone called out a line from Sandor Petofi's poem, "We vow we can never be slaves!"

That ignited a spark and over the next several days the anti-Soviet movement grew in numbers and strength. One elderly woman was quoted as saying, "We have been silent for eleven years. Now, no one will stop us." Government employees stripped the hated hammer and sickle from their uniforms and joined the students in the streets. Green, white, and red armbands and ribbons were seen everywhere. Down came Red stars from public buildings. The 25-foot bronze statue of Stalin was dismantled using acetylene torches, hammers, and metal pipes. One wrecker called out, "I want a souvenir of this old bastard!" The uprising spread throughout the country, and the Hungarian army joined the Freedom Fighters, as they were now called throughout the world.

In response, Soviet tanks rumbled into Budapest, and Soviet troops fired into the crowd, killing hundreds of unarmed people. Hungarians retaliated with gasoline bombs, destroying several Soviet tanks. Soviet soldiers armed with machine guns took up positions covering all bridges, boulevards, and public buildings. Martial law was imposed on the whole country and a 24-hour curfew on Budapest. Trains and streetcars stopped running; telephone communication with the outside world was cut. No one knew what was going on there, but we imagined the worst. Instead, we learned later, the Soviets were trying to save the situation by getting rid of the premier, old-line Stalinist Erno Gero, and replacing him with the more popular Imre Nagy, a "rightist" who encouraged nationalism. This, plus the tremendous show of Soviet force, put an end to the uprising.

Still, it would not go unpunished. Resistance leaders were being rounded up and sent in boxcars to the favorite Soviet prison, the Gulag in Siberia. Freedom Fighters liberated one thousand Hungarians from a train on its way east and dispersed them into the countryside. While the U.S. (or any Western country) did not go to the aid of the Hungarians, it did allow for the rescue of those seeking political asylum.

I agreed to sponsor one Hungarian refugee, a man named Carlo, who was coming to the U.S. under the sponsorship of the Tolstoy Foundation. The foundation was as usual helping an endless stream of refugees from totalitarian regimes come to America.

I was waiting at the bus station in Syracuse when Carlo's bus pulled up. There were two dozen refugees on it. The guide for the group, an American, began checking the names of the passengers against his list.

"I'm missing one guy," he said finally. "Where's that guy named Tolstoy?"

I tried to explain that Leo Tolstoy was a famous Russian writer, long dead, and certainly not in the group. The guide didn't believe me. "Tolstoy, a writer? Never heard of him. He'd better show up before I complete my list!"

Twenty-six years later I was attending a banquet on the roof of the St. Regis Hotel in New York City. A very attentive waiter whispered in my ear after the dinner, "My family and I thank you for all you did for us. I am Carlo—the Hungarian you sponsored to come to the U.S."

I was touched that he recognized me after so many years, and I was especially pleased to see him happy and doing so well here.

Living so far from New York City, which to us was still the cultural center of our lives, was very difficult. Often we visited for a weekend, driving the 300 miles from Syracuse each way nonstop. There we would shop for records and books that were not available in Syracuse and attend Broadway shows or concerts. We also kept in touch with friends there.

On one of our visits, I met a former Georgian prince. He asked me in a very supercilious manner what I did and when I told him, he said with a sneer, "So you work for the Americans as an engineer. I would never join their establishment."

"Oh?" I asked. "And what do you do for a living?"

"I wash dishes in a restaurant," he said haughtily.

It was the snow, however, that made us decide to return to New York City for good. Syracuse, located between Lake Oneida and the Finger Lakes, was beautiful in the spring, summer, and fall, but was miserable in the winter. Smack in the middle of the snow belt that stretched from Buffalo to Schenectady, we frequently had four to five feet of snow on the ground from December to March.

One of my early-morning chores was to dig my car out of the snow, often when the temperature was below zero. Sometimes the cars in the parking lot were completely covered and if I didn't remember exactly where I parked, I would dig out someone else's car and then have to start over when I found my own. One year I decided that I'd had enough—no matter how much I appreciated my working environment at GE and its management's attitude toward me.

And I was ready to work in a new field. I had had enough experience with an excellent American company and knew enough people in my field to take a chance. Several other GE engineers from our original group of eight were leaving at the same time. Shea was going to Knolls Atomic Power Lab.

I applied for a job at IBM Corporation. Although I was well known in my field, the chief of personnel there turned me down flat, saying that nobody knew me there, and therefore no one could give me a reference. Then he tried to soften his refusal by suggesting that I try again the next year.

"Here's a copy of our magazine, *Think*. Take it home to familiarize yourself with the company," he said.

It was the May 1956 issue. That evening I began to read it. Suddenly I recognized my photograph on page 26! I was holding a pocket-sized solar radio receiver, which was a novelty then. This was the radio I had developed at GE. Virginia was indignant.

"Take this magazine back to IBM!" she said. "See what the chief of personnel says about this!"

I decided not to because I wanted to avoid any embarrassment on his part. He would never hire me if he felt I was trying to prove him wrong. In retrospect, it was good that IBM turned me down because I got a much better job, one that offered me an almost unrestricted chance to develop my professional career.

After this incident, I made a few inquiries and learned that the engineering firm American Bosch Arma would be interested. They were then beginning to build a miniature guidance computer using transistors for the Atlas missile in preparation for the U.S. space program and were looking for a senior electronics engineer. The position sounded very exciting to me and Virginia was eager to move back to New York City. We gave notice and began to pack.

"The doors at GE will always be open for you," the director of the laboratory told me when I explained that I would be leaving. I was very much touched by these words of farewell. But my career was about to take off in another surprising direction—outer space.

Happy about their new freedom in the United States the Keonjian family regard personal freedom as their most valued possession. Shown Sunday night on a TV show. (1952)

Freedom Has Real Meaning:

Electronics engineer Edward Keonjian can smile now as he poses for a picture taken during his vacation with his wife Virginia, in the punishment stocks at Williamsburg, Va.

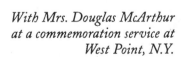

Williamsburg—not Leningrad

With Mrs. Douglas McArthur at a commemoration service at West Point, N.Y.

Holding the first solar-powered portable radio transmitter.

Depicting the solar-powered portable radio transmitter and its operation, in a comic book. It represents my family; Virginia, my son and myself (on the left). From G.E. comics "Adventures in Electronics", Dec. 1954.

SEVEN

On October 4, 1957, the Soviet Union launched a satellite into orbit. That event, a total surprise, electrified American scientists and politicians. *Sputnik*, as the 184-pound satellite was called, had been sent into its orbit 900 kilometers around the earth by a ballistic missile at a speed of 18,000 mph and immediately began sending continuous radio signals, "bleeps."

These were amazing facts with enormous implications for the United States. It meant that the U.S.S.R. had ballistic missiles, something unknown until that moment, and that its future satellites could monitor (or spy on) a variety of activities all over the world. The U.S. Air Force with its untested Project Vanguard and Project Far Side lagged behind the Soviet space program. The U.S. had sent rockets into the stratosphere, even rockets carrying animals, but we were a long way from being able to launch a satellite.

Even before the shock of this Soviet coup had died down, U.S. politicians were demanding that we "catch up." Congress authorized billions of dollars for a space program. It would eventually leave the control of the Air Force and become consolidated under the National Aeronautical and Space Administration (NASA). Funds for science education at all levels increased dramatically, and by 1961 a new president would promise "a man on the moon by the end of this decade."

I felt that the launching of Sputnik was a stunt, pure propaganda that served no purpose except to push the U.S. into the space race. Shortly after the launch I was asked to act as interpreter for a delegation of Soviet scientists who were visiting Columbia University in New York City. A prominent New York City matron joined us.

"Oh," she said to the Soviets, "we are so proud of what you have done! I'd like to give you a present to show you my esteem." She indicated a valuable painting.

"No," they told me without smiling. "No presents."

I tried to soften their refusal for her. She, thinking they were merely being modest, made the offer again, again stressing how proud she was of them. Again the answer was simply a very cold *nyet*. I suspected that they were under orders to not accept anything American, but I had a hard time explaining that to this woman, who couldn't understand why anyone would refuse her gift.

After Nikita Khrushchev came to power in 1958 the relationship between the U.S. and U.S.S.R. was characterized by confrontation and intense competition. John Foster Dulles, Secretary of State under Eisenhower, termed this maneuvering "brink-manship," because we were never far from the brink of nuclear war. Khrushchev called it "peaceful coexistence," but it was he who said, "We will bury the enemies of the Revolution!" to Vice President Richard Nixon, and that didn't sound very peaceful to anyone.

Soon after Khrushchev came to power, Fidel Castro and his mountain guerrillas deposed Cuban dictator Fulgenio Battista. Well-to-do Cubans abandoned their country and streamed into Florida when Castro, an avowed communist, began courting Khrushchev, seeking financial and military aid. Khrushchev responded with both. Just before President Eisenhower left office in 1961, he broke off diplomatic relations with Cuba. The U.S. CIA became nervous, watching the military build-up so close to this nation's shores. On April 17, 1961, a force of about 1,500 Cuban exiles, supported and armed by the U.S. government, landed in the Behia de Cochinas (Bay of Pigs) on the south coast of Cuba. They intended to foment an insurrection and overthrow Castro's Communist regime.

The invasion might have been successful if it had been supported by the U.S. Air Force, as originally planned. However, in the middle of the operation President Kennedy had a change of heart and refused to provide the badly needed air support. The consequences of this decision were catastrophic. Most of the invaders were killed or taken prisoner by Castro forces. Kennedy was severely criticized for his indecision in what became known as the Bay of Pigs fiasco. In December of 1962, Castro decided to "earn" some money for his government. He released 1,113 of the captured rebels in exchange for $53 million worth of American food and medicine.

Khrushchev, too, took advantage of the blunder. In August 1962 he began moving Soviet jet bombers and nuclear warheads into Cuba. In late October President Kennedy decided the time was right for confrontation. On October 22, he explained the situation to the American public on television. Soviet missiles with a range of 1,000 miles were already in place in Cuba. Kennedy charged that the presence of these weapons constituted a threat to the security of the nations of the Western Hemisphere and called for their immediate withdrawal. Otherwise, he was prepared to retaliate—also with nuclear weapons.

Americans were frightened, but stood behind their president. Virginia was frightened as well, but I knew that the Soviets would back down. Khrushchev was a bully and a man who loved to show off his power, but he wouldn't risk a nuclear war because he knew he would lose. Within the week he had written to Kennedy, declaring that he had issued an order for the dismantling of the missiles, with the conditions that the U.S. would never again invade Cuba and that the American missiles based in Turkey would be removed. Kennedy agreed. Under the watchful eye of reconnaissance pilots, the Cuban missiles were crated and shipped back to the Soviet Union.

Tensions were increasing in Europe as well, starting with cutting off all supply lines to West Berlin. Ironically, the strategy backfired. The U.S. came to the aid of the besieged city through an unprecedented mass airlift that prevented that city from succumbing to the Soviets. West Berlin prospered and grew, while East Berlin languished on the edge of poverty. In August of 1961 a fortified concrete barrier along the border between East and West Berlin was erected by the East

German Communist government to halt the vast numbers of East Berliners defecting to the West. Thousands of German families were separated as a result of the wall and hundreds of people, trying desperately to scale it, were killed by border guards. One of my favorite authors, John Le Carré, vividly described such an episode in his best seller, *The Spy Who Came in from the Cold.*

The Berlin Wall became a symbol of the intransigence of the Soviets and their fierce determination to control the future of Eastern Europe. Ironically, the strategy backfired, because democratic West Berlin prospered and grew, while East Berlin languished on the edge of poverty.

While world events were swirling around us, Virginia and I lived a quiet domestic life on Long Island, not far from the Garden City offices of my new employer, American Bosch Arma Corporation.

The company was located on Old Country Road in Garden City, Long Island, New York. In front of the main building was a stone monument, very insignificant in appearance, with an inscription. To my amazement it commemorated Charles Lindberg's solo transatlantic flight, which had taken off from this particular spot in 1927.

It was another of my coincidences to have my office windows facing exactly toward a monument to the hero of my youth, but I felt a pinch in my heart. How could such a great national hero as Charles Lindberg have such a small, inconspicuous monument erected at such a historic site?

Years later, in Locust Valley, Long Island, I was visiting my friend, the artist Zoric Ward, well known for painting members of the Senate and the Congress. Our conversation turned toward the beginning of the aviation era and the contributions made to it by such Russian-Americans as Sikorsky, De Seversky, and others. Discussing the Lindberg feat, she suddenly recalled how she, as an eight-year-old girl, had made her first flight sitting on Charles Lindberg's lap in his early flying days. She recalled that the plane had had difficulty clearing the woody area on a muddy airstrip, which is now the location of Garden City's Roosevelt Racetrack.

In 1993, long after I departed from Arma Corporation, I again visited the place where Lindberg's monument stood. It was gone. Later I was told it had been stolen a few years earlier. Money was being raised to restore it and place it in front of the Air Museum in Long Island, a couple of miles from the original location.

In 1983, while in the South Seas, I visited Lindberg's grave on the Island of Maui, next to the house where his widow lived. The grave was marked by a flat stone. Charles Lindberg was and still is my hero.

On Long Island, Virginia and I renewed old friendships and frequently got into Manhattan for concerts, the ballet, and the theater. We were thrilled with the innovative music and dance in *West Side Story* and I fell in love with *My Fair Lady*. We cheered when the great dancer Rudolph Nureyev defected from the Soviet Union in 1961 and wondered why the Beatles caused so much excitement.

My task with the Inertial Guidance Department of Arma was to miniaturize the size of the computer that was to be used in the Atlas missile. In 1959 I designed a prototype of an integrated circuit (IC), which represented a full computer adder. Since Arma did not have the capability to manufacture transistors, I asked J. S. Kilby of Texas Instruments in Dallas to put my primitive IC in a more acceptable form. He did. Thus the first prototype of the integrated circuit was born.

The importance of this device cannot be overemphasized. It accelerated the development of electronics in space technology, computer technology, avionics, medical technology, and ultimately in all phases of industry. It allowed for the emergence of robotics, a major step forward in manufacturing. It was a real breakthrough and I was very proud of having a hand in it.

Kilby and I presented a joint paper entitled "Design of a Semiconductor Solid-State Circuit Adder" at the 1959 International Devices Meeting in Washington, D.C., on October 29. It was considered "The most significant of three Integrated Circuits papers presented in that year."

Two weeks later, on November 16, at the 14th annual meeting of the American Rocket Society, also in Washington, I presented a paper entitled "Microminiaturization of Space Computers." My integrated circuit prototype transistorized adder was prominently displayed in the lobby of the Sheraton Park Hotel. A high-ranking delegation from the Soviet Union, consisting of several members of the Soviet Academy of Science, visited the exhibition. I had an hour-long lively conversation with them, in Russian, of course. Although the Soviet government considered me a "renegade," these scientists had a high enough status not to be afraid to be seen with me.

On April 19, 1960, I spoke to the members of the Radio Club of America, the oldest such club in the nation, which was made up of radio pioneers. My subject was "Microminiaturization and the Conquest of Space" and I discussed the feasibility of interplanetary travel within our lifetimes. I indicated that achieving that goal depended on the development of equipment capable of operating under the severe environmental conditions of space. Using reliable transistors in this equipment is the key to the success of such missions, I said. After I showed them the prototypes of integrated circuits and micro-miniature subassemblies with such circuits, we had a long and spirited discussion of what the future might hold. Flash Gordon was alive and well that night.

On my visits to West Coast electronic companies, I heard about Alexander Mikhailivich Poniatoff, founder of the giant AMPEX Corporation of Redwood City, California. A Russian émigré, Poniatoff had begun his company after tinkering with tape recording equipment in his garage. He wanted to produce high-quality recording equipment for professionals, especially musicians, radio stations, and broadcast companies. He named his company AMPEX by using his initials (A. M. P.) and adding "ex" for "excellency," because he was reputed to come from Russian nobility.

Singer Bing Crosby became interested in Poniatoff's enterprise and invested enough in it to get him out of his garage and into production. It was said that Crosby would sing only in studios which had AMPEX equipment. Since he was the most popular crooner in the nation at the time, that was a powerful incentive to acquire AMPEX recorders. Once the business was successful, Crosby sold his interest to

Poniatoff, who became its sole owner. He was a very wealthy man when I met him in 1961.

While I was in San Francisco attending a conference, Poniatoff invited me to join him for dinner at Alexis, a small restaurant known for its authentic Georgian food. The next day we met in his office to discuss the feasibility of transistorizing and miniaturizing AMPEX equipment. We spoke in Russian, because it was easier for both of us. I briefly told him what I knew about transistors and encouraged him to use transistors in his equipment.

After our talk, he took me to his home. In his bedroom were two giant TV sets—his and hers—mounted into the ceiling with remote controls for each. This was twenty years before the principle of remote control for television sets was widely accepted. Poniatoff's genius has been widely recognized both in industry and academics. In the 1970s the Poniatoff Chair in Physics was established at Stanford University. The first Poniatoff professor was Dr. William Shockley, my old mentor from the Bell Labs and a recipient of the Nobel Prize.

In the process of procuring transistors from various manufacturers, I stumbled across the problem that at that time transistor parameters were not standardized. That meant that selection and replacement of transistors were very difficult. Each new batch of transistors came with different characteristics and questionable reliability data, although it might have the same number as a previous batch. A joke that made the rounds years later emphasized this problem:

An astronaut was asked how he felt sitting in a rocket. He replied, "I'm not too comfortable, knowing that I'm sitting on top of 100,000 transistors of unknown reliability all purchased from the lowest bidder!"

I decided that the chaos in the industry was likely to get worse and hold us back. With this in mind, I contacted the Electronics Industries Association (EIA) and persuaded them to form committees on standardization of transistor parameters, the methods of testing their reliability, and on the requirements of transistor users. The latter committee would be made up of both commercial and military equipment manufacturers who actually use transistors.

I agreed to chair all the committees temporarily, although the objectives of each was different. Manufacturers of transistors wanted to make them as cheaply as possible without compromising too much on their performance and reliability, while users wanted to have transistors with almost infinite reliability at affordable prices. Sometimes my position was precarious, as I had to change hats frequently.

Despite the obstacles, in three years we were able to issue a series of useful standards, among them a noted MIL STD #883, as well as acceptable high standards for use in NASA programs.

Somewhere along the way I became an international "ambassador without portfolio" for the electronics industry. In spite of my accent, which was still pronounced, my speaking schedule was full and I addressed a wide range of subjects both in the United States and abroad.

I felt that these national and international meetings were very important for the smooth flow of international trade. Besides, thanks to electronics, we could not isolate ourselves from the rest of the world. Every nation on earth was now connected through radio, television, and jet travel. Since we were all neighbors, we might as well learn to be civil to each other. A good place to start was with science, which was the least likely topic to cause a cultural clash. I could see firsthand that peaceful cooperation among nations was possible on technical matters.

Being a world traveler changed my perspective on many things. A gourmet at heart, during my many trips abroad I never missed the opportunity to indulge in my mild "vice," especially after having suffered from malnutrition in the Soviet Union and Germany during World War II. I always enjoyed delicious food, good vintage wine, and stimulating conversation. One of my observations was that so-called "national dishes" in their native countries were a far cry from what we get in America. For instance, the pizza is much tastier in the U.S. than in Italy, while "Russian" restaurants in London offer Russian menus in name only.

Arma was very supportive of my "outreach" work. In October 1960 I was invited to participate in the 25th general meeting of the International Electrotechnical Commission (IEC) in New Delhi, India, which was devoted to various aspects of standardization in electronic equipment. Twenty-seven nations from both sides of the Iron Curtain were represented with a total of 459 delegates.

I was the chief U.S. delegate in committee 12-I on standardization of transistors. Because of alphabetical seating, I sat next to the delegate from the U.S.S.R., who happened to be my former technician at the Institute in Leningrad. All during the meetings he kicked me under the table while hissing at me, "You so-and-so! How could you defect to America?" Yet when he rose to speak, he referred to me as "my distinguished colleague from the U.S. on my right." And I, just as polite, referred to him as "my distinguished colleague from the U.S.S.R. on my left."

Our IEC meetings were held in the beautiful and comfortable Ashoka Hotel, which housed the entire secretariat (excellent stenographers, typists, translators, duplicating facilities), post office, telegraph, and banking services. It was near the U.S. embassy, an elegant architectural creation by Philip Johnson which emphasized openness and airiness. Almost next door was the Soviet embassy, which was built like a fortress with parapets and observation towers. The contrast was striking.

Another contrast was in their flags. The Soviet flag was large and its colors bright. Next to it, the American flag looked small, faded, and cheap. I asked the American protocol officer why our flag looked so pathetic. He replied that the hot Indian sun fades the colors very fast.

"But the Soviet flag is not faded," I pointed out. "Is the Indian sun less destructive to it?" There was no answer. "Well," I continued, "when I return home I will raise the question with the State Department." Two days later the American embassy was flying a large, brightly colored, new flag.

Informal receptions held during the conference allowed us to get to know our counterparts in other countries. I made many valuable professional connections which I would develop in the years ahead. And I learned that diplomatic skill is as important as high technical competence for scientists.

Near the end of the conference, the heads of each of the twenty-seven delegations were to be introduced individually to Dr. Radbakrishnon, the vice-president of India, at his palace. It seemed to me that everyone else had had a turn, but the Americans still had not been called. Then I learned that the ceremonies were almost over. I went to the chief of protocol at once and said that we had been over-looked.

"The United States does not like to be ignored," I reminded him. "It is still an important country, even if you may not like it." He looked at me impassively. Then I said, "We Americans share with you a love for freedom of speech. I'd like to take advantage of this and call a press conference to announce that the government of India somehow forgot our existence."

On hearing this, the chief of protocol immediately pushed me into the arms of the Indian vice-president, who was just about to conclude the ceremonies, and photographs were taken of us shaking hands in apparent warm friendship.

I had an opportunity to look around both New and Old Delhi on the weekends. New Delhi has the look of a modern British capital, which it once was, with parks, tree-shaded boulevards, and impressive public buildings, including the presidential palace. It was designed by the British with straight lines, rectangles, circles, and other geometric shapes. Old Delhi, on the other hand, is an extremely crowded crazy quilt of crooked narrow streets, twisting lanes, and dead-ends. Every-where are beggars, push-carts, bicycles, motorcycles, cars, vendors, and pedestrians—and the noise, smells, and confusion that crowds of people bring.

India is an ancient land, but it is also a new nation. It was only ten years old when I visited it. Jawaharlal Nehru, the prime minister then, believed in democracy *and* socialism and was trying to steer the republic between the Communist and non-Communist blocs. He called himself "nonaligned," but many Americans were distrustful of his aloof stance. Nehru had more problems with the People's Republic of China than with either the Soviet Union or the U.S. In 1962, 30,000 Chinese soldiers invaded the borders of northern India. They subsequently withdrew, while remaining stationed along the border as a reminder of China's power. But Nehru's first foe was the poverty of India itself.

After the conference I wrote in my report, "A brief stay in India wipes out all previous conceptions of 'poor,' 'needy,' and 'impoverished.' You do not have any conception of what these words can mean until you have seen India and view the forms which poverty takes.

"The Indian government strives desperately to raise the economic standards of the population, but my short stay left me with the impression that this is not a task that can be accomplished in a few years. Rather it may very likely require centuries for the results to be felt by a substantial majority of the Indian people. The Indians we come in contact with in the United States—government officials, U.N. personnel, and students—are not representative of the populace as a whole. They are the more fortunate and privileged groups. All the preconceived ideas I had about the country underwent drastic revision."

I couldn't get used to the contrast between beautifully designed and engineered buildings standing side by side with shacks, mud huts, and tents that housed the majority of the population. During this first trip to India I wasn't able to visit the homes of any of my fellow engineers. For the most part, these people were too self-conscious of their living standards in comparison with ours to invite us, and Americans were not very popular in India at that time.

However, I did visit a few Indian homes, arranged by the government. One of my hosts was a high government official who lived with his wife and two daughters in a modest five-room apartment—a luxurious place compared to most. His salary was $450 per month, among the highest in the country (and slightly below average in the U.S. then). He was able to employ four servants to help run his household.

The great majority of Indians did not know much about the United States, nor did they care to. They were primarily concerned with the daily battle for survival. For Indian children, though, America was a "fairy land" and no amount of government propaganda could change their minds. The few souvenirs that I gave to the children of one of my hosts caused such delight and pleasure that I will never forget it.

I received souvenirs as well. At one home, I accepted thirty-nine photographs of all the living and deceased relatives of my host. At that particular house, the entire neighborhood stopped by to bid me good-bye, wanting a first-hand view of an "American uncle."

On a later trip to India I was invited to the house of a maharani, widow of a maharaja. I had met her at a party at the American Embassy. Approaching her residence, we were met with a long row of servants holding torches to illuminate the entrance. After the usual pleasantries, my conversation with the maharani quickly became political.

"Frankly speaking," she said, "I do not like Americans."

"Why not?" I asked, somewhat perplexed because I knew she was a frequent guest at the American Embassy.

"Because after the war you Americans enriched yourselves considerably at the expense of our soaring population. Undoubtedly you have seen our poor, homeless, hungry children. You cannot miss them. They are everywhere you look."

I did not contradict her. "Yes, you are absolutely right," I said. "What do you think we should do to rectify such a terrible injustice?"

"It's very simple," she replied. "You have to distribute your wealth, which you unfairly acquired, among our poor children. Then we will all love you."

"Ahhh," I said thoughtfully, "that certainly seems to be the right thing to do. Suppose you set us an example by giving away a part of your wealth to these poor children in your country. It would be a wonderful gesture, and I'm sure we would follow your example."

"What!" she shrieked. "You suggest that I give my money to those dirty parasites? Never! I will not give a cent to those dogs."

Our conversation ended abruptly and I rushed for the exit.

On the final day of the conference, the Indian government gave a parting gift to each delegate, a kilogram of the best Indian tea in an attractive metal box, each with a commemorative label of our meeting. Unfortunately, most delegates had already packed their suitcases and did not want to unpack them to put in the tea, so they left the tea in their hotel rooms. I was not able to leave when the others did because I became ill, so I collected eighteen packages of the left-behind tea and brought them home to give to friends, as well as to enjoy myself.

One of the photographs I took in Old Delhi was shot from the interior of an old mosque, looking from the shadows to the bright light outside. An Indian family dressed in black was standing inside. At the entrance of the mosque in the bright sunlight, a European woman dressed in white carrying a white parasol was standing. The contrast was remarkable.

I submitted this photo to the 1962 World-Wide Photography Contest sponsored by *The Saturday Review of Literature*. To my surprise, it was selected as a finalist. Many years later, a Dutch friend, Annie Lels, visited me from Holland, where that photograph, among many others, was displayed on the wall. She studied the photograph for several minutes then asked me when it was taken. I told her.

"That's me," she said, pointing to the woman in white. I was dumbfounded, but we compared stories and I became convinced. Of the four billion people in the world, what are the odds of that happening? So many of these coincidences have occurred in my life and yet I never get used to them.

While in New Delhi, I was approached by a delegation from the Japanese company Fujitsu Limited, asking if I could stop in Tokyo on my return to the U.S. After visiting the company, I was asked if I would accept a consulting position with them. I agreed to, providing I would not have to relinquish my obligation to Arma and providing I could use only my vacations for consulting there. They found this acceptable and, in fact, offered to pay me a yearly fee for a few weeks' work, plus transportation for Virginia and me from New York to Tokyo and back.

Life in Japan fascinated me and I enjoyed my short visits to the fullest. In the early 1960s not many Western tourists visited Japan, and

Virginia and I were treated like royalty because of my business association with a Japanese company.

Japanese employment philosophy and policy are markedly different from ours. When an employee is hired there, especially in engineering, he is hired for life. The management considers him a member of their family. There is no jumping from company to company as Americans do, and the loyalty of the employee to his company is unmatched anywhere in the world. At the end of the year, all employees receive a one-half annual salary as a bonus which was timed to coincide with Christmas. This is another way to bind employees to the company.

Young women on the assembly line may live in dormitories paid for by the company. The Japanese system of requiring aerobic exercise during work breaks is well known and apparently more effective for productivity than our coffee-and-Danish breaks. I watched the young women at Fujitsu rush outside to play baseball during their "coffee breaks."

The work relationship between management and employee is strictly formal, but on weekends this relationship can become informal and familiar. It is not unusual for a manager to invite his employees to his house for a social gathering. On the other hand, it is very unusual for Japanese people to invite Americans to their houses. I was especially fortunate in this regard.

One day my boss, Mr. Omi, took me to his summer place on Lake Hakone about sixty-five miles from Tokyo. It was a medium-sized house on four high pillars with a unique entrance from underneath the house. After a hidden switch was tripped, a trapdoor opened and a retractable staircase descended. We went up and the staircase followed us. This was the only entrance to the house, so the owner did not have to be concerned about leaving his house unattended during his long absences.

Dr. Tagagi, the Dean of Tokyo University, invited me to dinner one night with his wife and seventeen-year-old daughter. The minute I was alone with his wife, she urgently asked me to take her daughter to a burlesque show sometime "for educational purposes" with the admonition, "Don't tell my husband!" I was very puzzled by this request, but gathered that the daughter had been asking to go, so I agreed.

Japanese burlesque opened at 9 a.m. and the shows were over by noon. So on a suitable morning we went, sitting on the front row. Miss Tagagi did not raise her head high enough to see anything during the entire performance, but when I asked her how she liked it, she replied, "Wonderful! I love it!"

Later, her father found out about our escapade and good-naturedly accused me of engaging in a conspiracy with his wife to spoil his daughter. I pled guilty.

Another family home I visited was that of Koji Kabayashi, president of National Electronics Company (NEC), "the GE of Japan." We were seated at a large table, he behind a small Japanese flag and I behind a small American flag. Soon I heard a commotion and noticed his wife approaching us on her knees, carrying the dinner tray. After she deposited the tray on the table, she left, also on her knees, without turning her back to us.

I commented to Kabayashi that he certainly had an obedient wife. He replied, "Don't be fooled. She is showing off just for you."

One day when Omi was in the U.S. he visited our home on Long Island, and Virginia quizzed him about his relationship with his wife. She learned that Mrs. Omi was the one who made all financial decisions, social plans, and domestic decisions. Virginia was very glad to hear this after I had told that all the decisions in Japan were made by the husband, not the wife.

Western wives also have a difficulty understanding Geisha houses. They are not houses of prostitution. Rather, they are places of total relaxation for men after a strenuous day at work, places to have fun in a very boyish way with good food and simple games. ("Scissors, paper, rock" is a favorite.) Geishas are trained from childhood to entertain. They may sing, dance, do magic tricks, tell jokes, or merely carry on an enjoyable conversation. They never demand anything, whine, or belittle their customers. They offer an oasis from the stresses of life.

An average Geisha house has six to seven Geishas under the supervision of an older woman who owns the house. Their kimonos are very expensive ($2-$3,000 each, when I was there) and must be changed often, both for aesthetic reasons and practical ones—they spend so much time on their knees that the front of the skirt wears out. Wealthy older men frequently act as patrons for Geishas, but this does not entitle them to a sexual relationship. When a Geisha is no longer young enough to entertain, her patron may buy out her contract and set her up as a bar or restaurant manager. A very wealthy patron might buy her a bar, providing security for the rest of her life.

I was enchanted during my first visit by a young Geisha whose demureness complimented her vibrant *joie de vivre*. Naturally I asked to see her again on my next visit, a year later. In my anticipation I arrived early. Up roared a motorcycle, and a rough-looking young woman in jeans dismounted. My Geisha! All my illusions were destroyed.

The Japanese respect for the elderly is legendary. Everywhere— in the office, in the stores, on the street—a man with white hair is a king. When an elderly person leaves a department store carrying packages, a young person would run to help him to the car. The Japanese would never consider sticking grandpa in a nursing home and forgetting him.

There are community baths in Japan, just as there were in Tiflis, but there is little comparison between the two. The one I visited in Tokyo was huge, like a small glassed-in football stadium, with three levels of pools. The lower pool was for men only, the middle pool for married couples, and the upper pool for girls and single women. Bathing is in the nude. The upper level is designed so that it can't be seen by men on the lowest level. Almost.

I found the Japanese food artistic but not very tasty. Fish is ubiquitous in Japan, and one grows accustomed to the flavor and smell of the sea. The fishy taste can permeate even the sweet treats, however, and I never developed a taste for Japanese candies.

My hosts were very fond of Chinese food and they liked French food as well. Now, the Japanese have adopted American fast food and like hamburgers as well as sushi. The most exotic restaurant I visited was Maxim's of Japan, which was three floors underground and furnished like Maxim's in Paris, with all-French decorations and a full French menu.

After my assignment was completed, I visited some resorts in the south of Japan. One was one of the most elegant I'd ever seen, with a giant swimming pool right on the beach. When the weather was cool, a glass partition was inserted to keep swimmers indoors; in warm weather the partition was lifted. The water came from hot springs and was altogether delightful. Each hotel in this area issued its own uniform to guests, a distinctive kimono. Mine was much too short. In their uniforms, tourists could be identified and brought back to the correct hotel if they got lost.

I stayed in a small, tastefully decorated inn in Tokyo. It had separate cottages, each surrounded by beautiful gardens. A small brook ran through the grounds creating a miniature waterfall. The peaceful sound of the water falling was almost hypnotic and quickly induced sleep. The inn had a novel way of ensuring that guests would pay their bill. During the night before check-out, an employee would sneak into your room and steal your shoes. The idea was that no one could leave barefoot. I had been warned about this "practice" and had brought another pair of shoes with me. But I paid my bill anyway and got my original shoes back.

Fujitsu was very solicitous of my comfort and often anticipated my needs. When I went shopping in the downtown area, a Fujitsu car followed me, in case I got tired and needed a ride. When I commented that I'd like to bring some Mikimoto pearls back as a gift for Virginia, several wives of Fujitsu managers descended on my hotel and took me to the main Mitumicha store in Tokyo. They spent hours sorting through the hundreds of necklaces available, seeking the best pearls, of the best size and luster, at the right price. Virginia was quite pleased with their choice.

Much later back in the States, a delegation from another Japanese company visited Arma. My boss asked me to act as interpreter.

"But I don't speak Japanese!" I said.

"It does not matter. You have such an accent you *must* speak Japanese," he replied. "Be at my office tomorrow at 2 p.m."

There was no arguing with him, his mind was made up. The next afternoon I was in his office at 2 p.m. On one side of the conference table was my boss and on the other side sat the Japanese engineers. I took a seat between them.

From the very first minute I saw that our visitors spoke better English than I did. Nevertheless, my boss completely ignored that fact. The interview began. My boss turned to me. "Ed, ask them how many days they expect to spend in our area," he said in English.

I turned to the Japanese. "How many days do you expect to spend in the area?" I asked the same question again in English.

The spokesman replied in English, "Four to five days."

I turned to my boss. "Four to five days," I said, also in English.

This entire "conversation," conducted exclusively in English, went on for more than half an hour. Days later I overheard my boss saying to someone, "Ed's such a perfect Japanese-English interpreter. You wouldn't believe it!"

After that, whenever anyone asked me how many languages I could speak, I would enumerate Armenian, Russian, German, English, and add "and Japanese!"

In June of 1961 I again represented the U.S. at the 26th general meeting of the IEC in Interlaken, Switzerland. From there on the way home, Virginia and I went to Paris. We stayed in a second-class hotel on the Left Bank, which was termed students quarters. Not luxurious at all. All night we were kept awake by the shouts of a man in the next room. As I tossed and turned, trying to get away from his voice, I fumed.

"Just wait until morning," I muttered to Virginia. "I'll knock on the door and when he answers, I won't even ask his name. I'll punch him in the nose!"

The next morning at eight o'clock, I indeed knocked on his door, still bursting with righteous indignation. Answering was a short, elderly man who asked kindly, "May I help you?"

I recognized him at once. This was the world-famous aerospace scientist Theodore von Kármán. He had developed the first shock tunnels, a variation on the old wind tunnels, to simulate missile reentry. A native of Budapest, he was now a U.S. citizen. He was the recipient of the first National Medal of Science, presented to him by President Kennedy.

How could I punch him in the nose? I couldn't. Instead I mumbled, "I just wanted to wish you a good morning."

"Come in, come in!" he responded expansively. "Have a cognac!"

Virginia and I joined him for a very pleasant morning, although we had to shout to be heard. Von Kármán was very deaf and that's the reason we had heard him shouting the night before. He'd been talking to friends in Paris on the telephone and like many deaf people, couldn't hear how loud he was. He was then the director of AGARD, the Advisory Group for Aeronautical Research & Development for NATO. Within a year of our first meeting, he appointed me to that group as a U.S. representative of the Avionics Panel.

Before we left Paris for New York, I wanted to take Virginia to a good French restaurant. We rented a taxi and the driver told us that he knew an excellent one a few kilometers from the city. We drove for quite a while and there was still no restaurant in sight. An hour went by. We began to worry.

Virginia asked me in Russian, "Do you think this was a good idea to go so far into the country so late at night?"

I replied that it wasn't a good idea and that we probably ought to turn back to the city.

"What if the driver refuses to turn back?" she asked. We apprehensively considered what the driver might have in mind for us. None of the possibilities was good.

"If he refuses," I told Virginia in Russian, "I'll jump him, wrestle the steering wheel from him, and push him over into the passenger seat. While I hold him down, you take over the driving."

She agreed. Just as we were about to implement our plan, the driver turned around and said in perfect Russian, "It is unnecessary. We are there."

Totally embarrassed, we slunk out of the car, giving the driver a large tip.

In July in Oslo I attended my first AGARD meeting as an observer. Virginia and I were vacationing there at the time. AGARD's mission is carried out through various panels, which are composed of experts appointed by NATO delegates. The appointments are normally for three years. In 1962 I was appointed for three years as a U.S. representative. However, on expiration of my term, I was reappointed for three more consecutive three-year terms, serving for a total of twelve years.

I was especially active as a Lecture Series Director, organizing and presenting international meetings, usually at leading universities of various NATO nations. These activities, while I was still on Arma's payroll, gave me a unique opportunity to meet scientists of various nations while increasing the breadth of my knowledge in microelectronics and its application to aerospace systems.

All of us in AGARD were of course very aware of the events taking place in Vietnam. In the early 1960s Vietnam was thought to be "another Korea," just a police action that would last a short time. The country had been divided after World War II into north and south, which quickly became Communist and anti-Communist. On November 1, 1963, Ngo Dinh Diem, who headed the South Vietnamese government, and his brother, Ngu Dink Nhu, were murdered in a coup. Madame Ngo, widow of the assassinated president, toured the United States, trying to get support for the Diem faction of the South Vietnamese government from President Kennedy and the Congress. She warned that without a U.S. commitment to destroying Communism in Vietnam, things would get worse. She also allegedly warned that President Kennedy would pay with his blood for what was happening in Vietnam. In three weeks he was assassinated.

Obviously, she was right on both counts. I was in Europe when the shocking news of Kennedy's assassination was broadcast and then the equally shocking murder of the alleged assassin Lee Harvey Oswald. I believed then and continued to believe today that Oswald, if he was involved at all, did not act alone. Perhaps we will never know who ordered Kennedy's assassination, but it certainly wasn't the idea of this pathetic failure of a man. The subsequent death of Jack Ruby, who murdered Oswald, made Kennedy's murder look suspiciously like a conspiracy to many Americans.

Earlier in 1963 I co-authored and edited the first comprehensive book on microelectronics, called *Microlectronics: Theory, Design, and Fabrication*. The contributors were among the most prominent leaders in their respective fields, including the talented and engaging Dr. Gordon E. Moore. It was delightful to have him as a valuable member of my AGARD team of scientists, who were giving lectures at various European universities. In later years he became Chairman of the Board of Intel Corporation and is the recipient of many national awards for his contributions to the semiconductor field (transistors, microelectronics, and microchips). On November 13, 1990, he was one of the recipients of the National Medal of Technology awarded by President George Bush. Our book was translated into many foreign languages and was chosen as the book of the month by the Control Engineering Book Club.

In June of the same year, 1963, I presented my first AGARD Lecture Series in Paris, France, and London, England. My team of speakers consisted of scientists from five different countries. Before the meeting started, the local British organizer of the meeting asked me if there might be some language barrier between my speakers and the English audience. I told him not to worry since we all now spoke a new international language: broken English. It satisfied the meeting organizer but not a lady seated in the front row. Hearing that someone in the last row was complaining that he could hardly hear me, she said, "I hear Edward too well. Would you like to exchange our seats?"

That year Arma lost a military contract which forced the termination of my association with that company. Subsequently I joined Grumman Aerospace Corporation at Bethpage, Long Island, first as a consultant and later as the chief of its Failure Analysis Laboratory. Looking back at my years at Arma, I feel that my association with that company was one of the most rewarding and interesting times in my professional career. The time spent traveling and representing my company in international organizations as well as on behalf of AGARD vastly expanded my knowledge of the world. It also permitted me to establish lasting friendships with many people abroad. I was especially gratified to form close and dear friendships with Arnold Geudeker and his charming wife, Hannie. Arnold was the able and efficient AGARD coordinator for the Netherlands, where he contributed so much of his effort to the success of our meetings.

At the American Rocket Society meeting, Washington, D.C. I display the first prototype of Integrated Circuit. On the left, the Soviet academicians Blagonravov and Serov.

Discussing the topic of micro-miniaturization with Chairman of the Board of Ampex Corp., Alexander M. Poniatoff.

At the reception in the Presidential Palace of India, in New Delhi. (I greet the Vice-President of India Dr. Radbakrishnon, on behalf of the American Delegation).

At the home of the Chairman of the Board of Nippon Electric Company.
Dr. Koji Kobayashi, the recipient of the Founders Medal, IEEE.

Presiding over the AGARD Seminar at the new University of Nice,
France, June, 1966.

EIGHT

On July 20, 1969, U.S. astronaut Neil Armstrong became the first human being to walk on the moon. I was fortunate to have had a role, however small, in that accomplishment. It is impossible to compute the effort, time, and resources that made the achievement possible. Although *Sputnik,* the beach-ball-sized artificial satellite launched by the Soviet Union in 1957, may have initiated the space age, the technology necessary for space travel has been developing since our primitive ancestors fabricated the first tool. Each step forward—wheel, arch, steamboat, automobile, airplane, eventually the satellite—has been an increment in what would become a triumph of human ingenuity and imagination.

President Kennedy had set the goal of placing a man on the moon and returning him to earth safely. The first stage in his plan was the Mercury program, but it was upstaged when the Soviet cosmonaut Yuri Gagarin completed a full orbit of the earth in *Vostok 1* on April 12, 1961. Our astronaut Gordon Cooper's 22-orbit mission in 1963 was bettered by the Soviet cosmonaut Nikolayev, who completed a 64-orbit mission in *Vostok 3,* while a Soviet woman, Valentina Tereshkova, was preparing for her 48-orbit mission in June of that year.

But in 1967, during the first mission of the Soviet spacecraft *Soyuz,* the pilot, V. Komarov, was killed. This tragedy and other disasters put the brakes on Soviet competition in the space race for a time. Then, after the U.S. successfully orbited Apollo VIII, circumnavigating the moon in December 1968, the Soviets abandoned their attempt to win the race.

Nevertheless, the quest to put a man on the moon was undertaken even without intense competition with the Soviet Union and required enormous technological development in all elements of space flight.

When I joined Grumman Corporation in 1964, it had been involved primarily in manufacturing military aircraft—the F-14, torpedo planes, the Wildcat, the Hellcat, and the Avenger. In the 50s, the company had invested in a $5 million Electronic Systems Center and started bidding on space contracts. They lost most of them—the orbiting solar observatory, the Nimbus weather satellite, and the Saturn rocket. But they didn't give up and finally won the LEM contract.

Originally employed as an electronic development engineer, I later became chief of the Failure Analysis Laboratory. My job was to analyze the potential and actual failures in electronic parts tested for the Apollo project and other electronic systems. It was also my job to suggest the necessary corrective action to avoid those failures. The electronic gears in the Apollo projects required a great amount of microelectronics in all their development phases. This was where my expertise was most useful.

The Lunar Exploration Module, called LEM or simply LM, built by Grumman for Apollo XI, was a squat, ungainly, four-legged pod that looked like a big metallic insect ("the bug"). Its shape was strictly functional, and there was no need to design it aerodynamically since the surface of the moon is airless.

On July 16, 1969, Apollo XI, carrying three astronauts—Neil A. Armstrong, Edwin Aldrin, Jr. ("Buzz"), and Michael Collins—was launched for landing on the moon. It was the most critical moment in the Apollo program to date. NASA's credibility and the program's future were at stake, as were the lives of three courageous men.

The world was watching. Thirty-four hours into the flight, the astronauts began broadcasting on live color television. Over 500 million people heard Aldrin comment that the view of the earth as it receded behind them was "out of this world." The feat was the most remarkable achievement of the American space venture.

After two lunar orbits, while the *Apollo* was on the far side of the moon, the astronauts undocked the LM—the *Eagle*—from the Command Module—the *Columbia*. Armstrong and Aldrin, who would walk on the moon while Collins piloted the *Columbia*, took the *Eagle* down with instruments and visual landmarks, a program alarm showing the on-board computer to be overloaded. It was a tense moment, and at the time of landing on June 20, 1969, Armstrong's heart was beating at 156 beats per minute, twice its usual rate. "Tranquility base here," he said calmly. "The *Eagle* has landed."

An entire society, factory workers and engineers, clerks and scientists, had participated in this breathtaking event.

Later Apollo projects continued to explore the moon. In August 1971, Apollo astronauts operated a $12 million, 460-pound roving vehicle, designed and built by General Motors and Boeing, on the moon's surface. In two days the moon rover covered more than fourteen miles of territory around the landing base. The Russians were stunned. "You Americans take your cars wherever you go, even to the moon," was the typical reaction.

There were other events, certainly, taking place in the world besides those related directly to my work. The year 1967 was remarkable for the Arab-Israeli War and the defection of Joseph Stalin's daughter Svetlana. The following year brought the Soviet invasion of Czechoslovakia. Though they were on the periphery of my immediate concern, these events and others—the Vietnam War, the disturbing student unrest in the sixties—contributed to the general malaise that was evident everywhere.

I could not comprehend how we ever got involved in that disastrous war. Couldn't we have learned a lesson from the French, who had suffered so greatly in Vietnam in the past? Why do countries not learn from history? Hitler made a similar mistake when he marched on Russia, disregarding Napoleon's fate almost 200 years ago.

Who can forget the amazing pronouncement of the late U.S. President Lyndon B. Johnson? "We are not in Vietnam to win the war" (which had already taken the lives of many thousands of Americans). What a waste!

During the waning years of the Apollo program, a colleague of mine from the NASA Center in Cambridge, Massachusetts, visited Virginia and me in New York. A top NASA official and a prominent scientist, he was en route to a conference in Moscow at which the Soviets had invited him to present a paper. He was very proud of the invitation and had determined to present his talk in Russian.

His last evening with us, we invited him to read his lecture to us, in Russian. He was delighted. Virginia and I listened attentively for 35 minutes and failed to understand a single word. His accent was atrocious. I gently suggested that it might be better to speak English, so that at least *some* Russians would understand him. He agreed but was clearly disappointed, especially considering the amount of money he had spent to learn Russian at the Berlitz School.

Looking over his English text, I noticed that some parts appeared to be of a classified nature. When I asked if he had received proper clearance, he answered, surprised, that as a scientist he required no clearance, even with his high rank. I pointed out that the Soviet Union was not a remarkably benevolent country and that his superiors might feel a need to authorize his presentation. But he refused to listen, saying that scientists from different countries should be able to communicate with one another without restriction, for the sake of promoting "the World Peace." I later learned that at the airport government officials prevented him from boarding the aircraft bound for Moscow. I can imagine how outraged this utterly naive man must have been.

Grumman encouraged my outside activities, which were numerous and demanding. Before and during my Grumman employment, I had been very active in professional activities such as chairing various Electronic Industries Association (EIA) standardization committees and participating in AGARD.

The year I joined Grumman, I presented a paper on micropower electronics at the International Solid State Circuit Conference in Washington, D. C. A year earlier, I had taken an AGARD team of scientists to an international conference in Germany of which the stated purpose was to demonstrate the utmost importance of reducing power dissipation in microcircuits employed in electronic equipment—that is, to achieve higher reliability. My team consisted of leading American and European scientists in the field and included G. M. Moore, J. L. Moll, W. W. Geartner, A. T. Watts, B. A. Boulter, R. C. Baron, and J. D. Meindel. (During the conference, one observer made the perplexing comment, "Here in Germany, we are always thought to get maximum power from any gear. Now we have to learn how to reduce that power to very minimum, very funny.")

As the conference organizer, I had to employ a combination of diplomacy, tenacity, organization, and thorough knowledge of the field. For such an effort, the work usually begins at least a year in advance.

First the conference topic is chosen. Then the chairman assembles a team, choosing from hundreds of esteemed professionals around the world. In doing so, he must rely on his (and only his) personal knowledge of the prospective speakers or their published works and reputations.

Then the chairman begins the tedious process of negotiating with each candidate, formulating the details of that participant's paper to be compatible with the rest of the program. Occasionally the chairman encounters a "prima donna" who insists upon presenting his paper without regard for the other members of the team. The choice then is to try to change his mind or drop him from the program. Finally the program is finalized, printed, and distributed.

It is a complicated process with diplomatic overtures, endless correspondence and long-distance calls all over the world, and a great deal of persuasion and commitment. I enjoyed doing it and apparently did a good job, since AGARD kept me twelve years as a U.S. member of its Avionics Panel and Director of its Lecture Series.

Once at an IEEE convention in New York I met a Soviet engineer, and we discussed the subject of mutual exchange of scientists and engineers between the U.S. and the U.S.S.R. He recalled the previous year's visit of an American group visiting Soviet electronic manufacturing plants and laboratories.

The things the Americans had seen were rather outmoded and

showed that the Soviets had a long way to go to even come close to American technological standards. Nevertheless, the Soviets were trying to make the Americans believe that their products were as good as those in the U.S. Hypocritically, the American delegation agreed with the claims and praised the products, although among the components some were of American origin and had not been used back home for more than fifteen years.

Only one member of the delegation, Robert Sprague, president of Sprague Electric Company of North Adams, Massachusetts, did not hesitate to express his opinion in a very undiplomatic way. "My God!" he said. "This is junk! How can you use it in your products? Why don't you learn to make better stuff?" The rest of the delegation was embarrassed by his outburst.

The Soviet engineer I was speaking to commented, "They were very nice people, but so gullible! They believed everything we told them. However, there was one smart man in the group who appraised everything realistically. We could not fool him!"

"What was the name of this smart man whom you liked so much," I asked.

"Robert Sprague," he said.

It should be pointed out that, in general, Russians do not like to be praised by foreigners for things they themselves do not believe to be true. They consider such praise an insult to their intelligence, or else evidence of extreme naivete. By the same token they respect those who criticize them justly.

In October 1965, I was the American delegate to the meeting of the International Electrotechnical Committee in Tokyo. We stayed at a small Japanese inn, which had a bathtub the size of a small swimming pool. Virginia was told that she could take her bath in the nude, which she did. Fifteen minutes into her bath, two couples showed up, also in the nude. Paying no attention to Virginia, they entered the tub. She didn't share their nonchalance, however, and made a mad dash for our room. It was her first and last Japanese communal bath in the nude.

Often accompanied by a guide from the Fujitsu Company, we

toured Kyoto, Nara, and other cities. We took the famous Bullet Train to Kawasaki and visited popular Lake Hakone, a favorite Japanese vacation spot. Twice we visited the home of Tokyo University professor H. Inose and his beautiful wife, Niko. Years later I had the pleasure of seeing the Inoses in the U.S. on a few occasions. Tokyo University dean Tagaki and Mr. Omi of Fujitsu were also gracious hosts.

This was my second trip to Japan but the first with Virginia, with whom I could share my impressions on the spot. As I expected, our stay in Japan was inexpressibly delightful. Could we fail to be enchanted by a country that legend claims was created by a descendant of the sun goddess, ancestor of the emperors who ruled for centuries by divine right? It is a mystical place, its mountains and narrow valleys peppered with some 60 active volcanoes, all in an area about the size of Montana. Nearly 125 million people live in that enigmatic land, growing rice and vegetables, manufacturing machinery and electronics—and learning. With an extraordinary literacy rate of 99 percent, the Japanese are among the world's best-educated people. We found our Japanese friends to be intelligent, learned, hospitable, and more. They demonstrated in small but picturesque ways their awareness of the rhythm and artistry of the dance of life.

One day at Tokyo University, I was warned not to leave the building. A raucous student demonstration, deceptively noisy, was being staged by what turned out to be a fairly small group of participants. One of the professors directed my eyes toward video cameras on nearby rooftops.

"The students are demonstrating for *their* benefit," he said, pointing to the cameras. "When the cameras leave, the demonstration will stop."

He was right, and in less than half an hour, the campus was quiet again. To this day, I don't know what the demonstration was all about. Perhaps it was an isolated incident addressing some perceived dishonor or wrongdoing on the part of the university; or it may have been a specimen of the sporadic unrest that sometimes surfaces in a country that, while prosperous, suffers from severe air and water pollution, urban congestion, and housing shortages. Occasionally, grassroots movements arise to oppose the use of nuclear energy. The Japanese have not forgotten Hiroshima.

We returned to New York forever enriched by our Japanese experience. It was a time of great joy. I arrived to discover that I had been granted the prestigious Fellow Award of the Institute of Electrical and Electronics Engineers (IEEE). Eighteen years earlier, at the IEEE annual convention, I had admired the distinguished scientists whose professional achievements had earned them this same high award. To me they were supermen. I had been awestruck with admiration, and I had almost expected them to accept their awards and fly out the window. It had been a bit of a letdown to see them leave the stage, calmly and unceremoniously, on foot, like ordinary mortals, as I did on January 1, 1965, when the award was presented to me. I also did not fly and walked away as an ordinary mortal.

Our son's engagement was another great blessing. His bride-to-be, Bobby Youel, was bright and exuberant, the daughter of a prominent San Diego orthopedic surgeon, Milo, and his vivacious wife, Helene.

Despite many ups and downs, Virginia and I had always managed to look on the bright side of life. If there was any remaining shadow, it was in Virginia's longing for a daughter. We were overjoyed to receive Bobby into our lives, as our own child. She enchanted us with her laughing eyes and effervescent personality, and with her unequivocal love for Karik, a love that was wholly returned.

A few months before the wedding, Milo and Helene came to New York to meet us. There was some awkwardness at the beginning; our accent was alien to them, but in just a few hours we were communicating with ease and friendship. We were comfortable and compatible, and delighted to learn that our family had gained not only a daughter but the kinship of her parents as well.

Milo and Helene had planned to hold the reception in their San Diego home. They had invited all their relatives and many friends, nearly a hundred people in all. How many of our relatives would be attending the reception, they wondered.

"We have no relatives or friends who would be able to travel to San Diego for the wedding," we replied.

They were surprised.

"Everyone has relatives!" they insisted. "Why not you?"

It was difficult to explain to the Youels, who were blessed with a million relatives, that as refugees from the Soviet Union we had left our families behind the Iron Curtain. Milo and Helene continued to be perplexed and unconvinced. To ease their minds, I decided to simply create some temporary "relatives." I was the chairman of several EIA committees, and many of my colleagues on those committees lived in Southern California. I telephoned some of them, asking if they would be my relatives for a day and attend the wedding. On the appointed day, my relatives started to arrive and the occasion proceeded without a hitch.

A friend of our in-laws in San Diego gave us a huge party around the pool at his spacious villa. There were close to a hundred people attending, all completely unknown to me. We all had I.D. tags on our jackets. At the end of the party, I started saying good-bye to everyone, shaking hands. Finally, at the exit, there was one more man, whose hand I reached to shake. "What is your name?" I asked politely. He pointed to his tag. It said, "I live here."

Virginia and I had decided to give the couple our Buick convertible as a wedding gift. Since I was scheduled to be abroad until just before the wedding, we decided that Virginia would make the trip alone. To make her solo journey safer, we advertised in a newspaper for a couple who would join her for a free trip to San Diego. After interviewing several prospective candidates, we selected a young couple that appeared more trustworthy than the others, though we were still a little apprehensive about a six-day trip with total strangers. Fortunately, Virginia arrived safely in San Diego, and I joined her just in time for the wedding.

The wedding itself was especially poignant for Virginia. She said she felt she was in heaven. After the reception, we drove the newlyweds to the airport, where they would board a plane to Mexico for their honeymoon.

As Karik and Bobby began climbing the stairs to the plane, my son noticed in horror that I was following them with a suitcase in my hand.

"Where are you going, Father?" he shouted.

"I am going with you to your honeymoon," I shouted back with all the seriousness I could muster.

My son was in a panic. He ran to his mother, pleading, "Tell Father he is not in the wild Caucasus; this is America! He can't come with us!"

Virginia tried to calm him down. "Do not pay attention to what your father said. Go ahead to Mexico and enjoy the honeymoon. I will keep your father here and will not let him go with you."

I still do not know if my son knew that it was a joke or if I was serious. Certainly it was not the first time he had found himself the object of my jokes, however harmless.

After the honeymoon, Karik and Bobby moved to Tucson, Arizona, where both were enrolled at the university.

Not long after, I was due to be at an AGARD meeting in Milan. I had forgotten my departure date, and when the airline called to say that my flight had been delayed, I asked myself, "What flight?" Only then did it occur to me that I might be missing a meeting I was scheduled to chair the following day. I rushed to the airport in such haste that I forgot to put on my street shoes. On the plane, staring at my slipper-clad feet, I realized my oversight.

The meeting was scheduled for afternoon, so I had a little time after arriving in Milan to buy a pair of shoes. Unfortunately, it was hard to find my size—12-1/2—in Italy. After searching through many shoe stores without success, I finally bought the largest pair of Gucci shoes available, a size-and-a-half smaller than I normally wore.

In the afternoon, wearing my new shoes, I opened the meeting, but I was in such pain that it was obvious to the audience that something was wrong. Finally, I decided to tell the audience what had happened and asked permission to take my shoes off.

The audience was sympathetic, the shoes came off, and I proceeded to lead a three-day conference in my stocking feet. At some of the official receptions, I had no choice but to keep my magnificent but torturous shoes on. (Back in New York, I tried to stretch them so I could wear them once in a while. They were too beautiful and too expensive to throw away. I had no luck, however, and eventually had to give them to one of my friends.)

The AGARD meeting was in the splendid museum of Leonardo da Vinci, supreme genius of the Renaissance. The museum houses hundreds of his projects—wooden models of flying machines, hydraulic pumps, and various other inventions—all executed with scientific precision and consummate artistry. Filled with awe and admiration, I wondered how the man who had created these mechanical marvels hundreds of years before his time could be the same person who painted the celebrated *Mona Lisa, Adoration of the Magi, Madonna of the Rocks, The Last Supper,* and other masterpieces. Inexplicably, the museum was not well attended and its halls were empty most of the time.

At the end of the conference the U.S. consul gave a party in my honor, attended by many other foreign consuls. Seated across the table from me was a middle-aged woman, Musa Silver, the Finnish consul and head of the diplomatic corps in Milan. We enjoyed a very spirited conversation, and close to midnight, with the party getting louder and louder, Musa suggested that she and I retreat to her apartment for a cup of coffee. I readily agreed, for she was an engaging conversationalist with a wealth of knowledge about Italy gleaned from her twenty-five years in the country.

Musa lived in a tastefully decorated apartment on the ninth floor of a modern building in downtown Milan. It was filled with mementoes of her travels through Europe. On her grand piano were autographed portraits of famous Finnish artists, composers, and musicians.

After a marvelous hour of coffee and conversation, I was preparing to leave when she asked me to sign her huge guest book, if possible, in four languages I knew: Armenian, Russian, German, and English. While she momentarily left the room, I glanced through some of the back pages to see who had been there before me. There were many signatures of people unknown to me. Then suddenly I found the name of my good friend and colleague from Leningrad, Professor Moskvitinov! I was flabbergasted. How could he be in Milan?

"Yes," Musa said. "He is my friend. He lives in Milan now. Would you like to see him?"

"What a question!" I shouted. "Let's telephone him!"

My friend's reaction to hearing my voice was indescribable. He came over right away, and we embarrassed each other greatly, almost weeping in the excitement of meeting again after so many years.

We spent hours telling each other our personal stories while Musa served us tea, cookies, and other Italian delights. It was already 3:15 a.m. when she decided to invite another friend of hers, Mr. Heikenen, the American consul in Milan and a confirmed bachelor. He arrived at 4:00, and Musa began to serve us an early breakfast that lasted almost another two hours.

My friendship with Musa continued for many years. When I would visit Milan, she would teach me how to bargain in Italian shops, how to check inflated restaurant bills, how to negotiate taxicabs, and other survival skills. "Do not trust those Italians," she would say in jest. "They are all crooks." Yet she took me to many private Italian art exhibits and music performances in the homes of her Italian friends, whom she adored. Apparently in her eyes they were not among the "crooks."

When I visited Milan with Virginia, Musa again played host to us. We traveled with her to parts of Italy I had not seen before. Occasionally Mr. Heikenen would join us, and we had a great time.

Once Musa took us to the Canonica Restaurant, fifteen miles from Milan. "This is the place," she told us, "where Italian husbands bring their lovers." We noticed a young couple—a short, stocky Italian man with a six-foot-tall Swedish girl. He was all over her on the street and not the least embarrassed by our presence.

The restaurant was famous for its delicious food. Italian cuisine offers such a delightful variety of subtle flavors and textures, from the luxuriant thickness of minestrone to the delicate frothiness of zabaglione, a foamy wine dessert made with egg yolks. (Once, at an elaborate banquet given by the Italian government in honor of our delegation, I was mortified by an American guest who refused to eat because there were no hot dogs on the menu.)

Olive oil pervades Italian cooking. Italy leads the world in the production of olives, which thrive on the country's stony hillsides and need mild winters and a long, hot growing season to survive. Millions of acres in Italy are also planted in grapes. In the Po Valley, intensively farmed, vines for grapes are strung between fruit trees so that every bit of space is used productively.

Italian grapes have a flavor all their own, and as we were leaving the Canonica, the proprietor treated us to an excellent Italian wine in front of the restaurant. "All on me," he said gallantly. While we were drinking our wine, a truck stopped and the driver asked if we would permit him to sing for us. Soon the air was full of music, excerpts from popular Italian operettas. The driver had a remarkable voice, but the poor fellow had not a single tooth in his mouth.

About ten minutes later a second truck stopped. The driver emerged with a violin and joined our group, accompanying the singing driver of the first truck. Soon the street was blocked as two more trucks with musical drivers stopped. Traffic was at a standstill until the impromptu concert ended. I had never seen anything like it in my life. "This is Italy," I said to myself. "Where else could it have happened?"

I had the presence of mind to photograph the scene as it progressed from beginning to end. Now I look at those photographs with great nostalgia. *Viva Italia!*

While in Italy, Virginia and I went to Venice. After two days there we visited a little island called San Lazzaro, which was given to the Armenian monk Mechitar in 1717 by the Catholic church as a reward for the monastery having accepted Rome as its head. On San Lazzaro Mechitar built a monastery that became famous all over the world for housing the largest Armenian library outside of Armenia. Among several non-Armenian scholars and poets who studied in the library was Lord Byron, who translated Armenian poetry into English.

His room is still there. The Armenians in San Lazzaro belong to the Uniats Christians under the order of the Mechitarists. They have kept the Gregorian rites and the language but are subordinate to the Pope of Rome.

In 1967, the AGARD meeting was held near Bologna in the historic Villa Grifone, the birthplace of Guglielmo Marconi, inventor of the wireless (radio). It was a thrill to visit the two-story villa where Marconi had successfully demonstrated his invention. The world's first radio signal was transmitted from a ground-floor window. The inventor's brother, a distance away behind some bushes, discharged his pistol to confirm that he had received the signal.

This was in 1895, the start of radio communication, a new era of human progress. The site of the window was strangely familiar to me. Its photograph had been in my school scrapbook in Tiflis. Would I have believed then that almost a half-century later I would be standing at that very window?

At the end of the conference I was invited to say a few words for a Rome television station in connection with the thirtieth anniversary of Marconi's death. I spoke in English, but back in New York, viewing the tape the Italians had given me, I was amazed to see myself speaking in Italian! The dubbing was perfect.

The following fall, Virginia and I were in Cambridge, Massachusetts, where I was to conduct a microelectronics symposium at M.I.T. Virginia returned to New York before me, taking her small suitcase with her. On the opening day, standing on the podium, I opened my suitcase to take out my picture slides and lecture notes. Instead I found myself holding a variety of ladies' garments, brassieres and stockings and nightgowns. I was totally embarrassed, but the audience was delighted.

I explained to the chairman what had happened and asked that my talk be canceled since my notes and slides had gone to New York. But the chairman was unmoved and did not even find the situation funny, insisting that I proceed with my presentation. I had no choice but to talk about what was on my slides, the diagrams the audience couldn't see. To my surprise, they liked the presentation and applauded me heartily for it. After the meeting, the chairman turned to me and said, "Ed, you pulled a clever trick on all of us and it worked beautifully. Next time I'll try to use it in my presentation."

At the conclusion of the seminar, the faculty took me to dinner at an elegant restaurant. After ordering the meal, my colleagues asked me to select a wine from a list of more than two hundred brands. When I asked why they wanted *me* to do it, they replied that with my accent I was better qualified to make the right choice. Once again, I found myself in a dilemma because of my accent.

I was staring at the list of unknown-to-me brands of French and other wines while my associates and the maitre d' waited impatiently. Finally, I resorted to an old trick: to select wine by price, not by brand name. I chose the most expensive bottle, Chateau d'Yquem of 1947 vintage. The price was $85.

The maitre d' seemed surprised. "Are you sure you want this wine?" he asked.

"Of course," I replied with wounded dignity. "I always drink this wine. Only chill it properly."

The wine was served. It was a sweet wine. Although most of us had ordered steak, everyone liked my choice and complimented me on my expertise.

The flattery went to my head, and I began to believe that I had indeed made an excellent choice. I took the label from the bottle and determined to buy myself a bottle of the same wine. The next time I was in Paris, I took the label to the French stores and tried to buy the wine. "Go to Boston or New York," was the reply. "We don't drink it in France; it's for export only."

In 1970 I chaired an AGARD conference in Istanbul. Also called Stamboul, it is the only city in the world situated on two continents. The ancient Turkish city lies on both sides of the Bosporus, part of the narrow strait that separates Europe from Asia. The city straddles the Golden Horn, an inlet of the Bosporus that forms a superb harbor. Formerly known as Byzantium, then Constantinople, Istanbul was, like

Rome, built on seven hills. The magnificent Hagia Sofia, originally a Greek Orthodox church, was converted into a mosque after the Ottoman conquest in 1453. Now it is a museum.

When the conference ended, the Turkish government entertained us at a night club where a belly dancer was throwing her scarf on the guests, inviting them to dance with her. I volunteered, and when the dance was finished, the club owner whispered to me, "Come again to dance with my girls. You will get a free meal."

An American gentleman in the audience was entertained by my performance and took photographs. When he identified himself as the American consul, I was chagrined, but he waved away my embarrassment. "Only a red-blooded American like you could get away with it," he smiled. "I congratulate you for your great spirit. Do not worry; you were on the ball."

Two months later, he sent me the photographs.

During our visit we strolled the beautiful city and indulged in delightfully tasty seafood. Many times we ate freshly caught fish that were fried on kerosene stoves right on the fishing boats.

The day before I was to leave, I became ill. The next day our delegates flew home, while I remained in the hotel with a high fever. After I recovered, I tried vainly to get a new airline reservation, although Pan American jets were leaving the city practically empty. After four days of intense "negotiation" with the Turkish authorities, I was able to board a flight to Athens. Whether the obstacle had been my Armenian surname or simply the monumental Turkish bureaucracy, I was never certain. In any case, I was glad to leave.

Virginia had always been keenly interested in space exploration and read everything she could find on the subject. She had closely followed the preparation of the LM and was proud that her husband had had a part in it, however small. On a television set in a hospital room, she watched some of the early Apollo missions.

In 1967 we had learned that Karik and Bobby had decided to "split" (as he put it). We were totally unprepared for the news, since we hadn't realized there was anything wrong in their marriage. The trauma was particularly great for Virginia. She took it as personally and pain-fully as if her own life was being broken. I do not believe that she ever recovered from the shock. Less than two years later she passed away, just a few months before the historic landing on the moon. The medi-cal cause of death was cancer of the intestine, but the divorce had left her spiritually broken before she became ill. Even when we bought a charming summer house on Lake Zohr in Connecticut fully furnished to the smallest detail, spending weekends there with friends, she never completely enjoyed it. She would not stay there alone, even for a week. Eventually, I sold the house. There was no reason to keep it after Virginia's death.

The house was in the middle of the woods just two miles from the Russian village Churaevka, where several of our friends had homes. A natural wall of evergreens surrounded the back yard. There were magnificent perennial flower beds—irises, daisies, poppies—and breath-taking roses. We enjoyed the company of our friends on the back porch, always sunny and inviting, a place to watch all kinds of animals come for food. In the fall there were the spectacular colors of the leaves on trees near the house. Even in winter it was cozy; a warm fire could brighten our moods instantly.

On weekends we visited our friends for noisy but companion-able parties, or they came to us to collect mushrooms in our woods. They knew the difference between the good ones and the poisonous ones.

During the week the house was unattended, and there was al-ways the possibility of burglary. We had a large liquor supply, and when we were away we kept it in the stove, out of sight should there be in-truders. Arriving there one chilly afternoon, we quickly started a fire in our haste to warm the house. Soon there was a cannonade of exploding bottles and within half an hour the house was engulfed in flames. I don't remember how we were able to extinguish the fire and save the house from complete destruction. But we managed, and the episode became known among our friends as "the Keonjians' way to warm their house."

Virginia's death depressed me for a long time. It was difficult to get used to the absence of my life's companion, after being together through 37 years of good and bad fortune. Together we had shared the ordeal of living under Stalin's terror and Hitler's slave labor camps, and the problems we encountered during our first years in the U.S. without friends, money, or knowledge of the English language. Now, with these troubles behind us, having built a fine life in this wonderful country, it was a bitter irony that she was gone, so unfair that we must be apart.

In 1970 I decided to terminate my four-year consulting agreement with the Japanese firm Fujitsu, Limited. Although they wanted me for another year, they had learned the ropes in my field so quickly that my further counsel, I felt, would not be of real value to them.

At 6:00 the morning of my final departure from Tokyo, the entire family of my boss, Omi, including all his children and grandchildren, came to the airport to see me off. As we were saying our farewells, Mr. Omi handed me a package and urged me to open it. It contained a heavy silver picture frame in which was a photograph of Virginia, whom they had come to love during our visits with them. I was deeply touched and wondered how they had found a picture of her to give me.

"We loved Virginia-San" (this is how they called her). "She will always live in our hearts," they said.

The family had brought another surprise as well. They introduced me to a middle-aged Japanese lady in a smart European outfit. She had a suitcase and was holding an airline ticket for the same flight I was about to take.

"This is Niko," Mr. Omi said.

"How do you do?" said I. "What a pleasant surprise, to have such charming company on the flight to the States."

"It is no coincidence that Niko is flying with you," said Omi. "We selected her through a large computer service that came up with four candidates. We made the rounds and finally selected Niko for you."

"For me? Just to accompany me on the flight?"

"Not exactly. She will stay with you in New York to comfort

you in your grief. Then, if you like her, you can marry her."

This was a shock to me! I could never have expected something like this, and I was petrified, not knowing how to react. If I refused to take her with me, my friends, who had gone to so much trouble to get her for me, would lose face. On the other hand, if she came with me and we found that we were not compatible, she would have to return home to face her people's condemnation.

Niko spoke good English. Buying time to think of a way out of this most confusing situation, I asked her if she spoke any languages besides her native tongue and English.

"Russian," she replied.

"How come?" I asked. "Russian is not popular in Japan."

"I spent six years in Chinese jails with my father," she explained. "When he died I was released, and here I am back in Japan."

During our short conversation, I learned that she was a concert pianist and was accomplished in many other areas as well. Decidedly my Japanese friends did not do things halfway.

Having recovered somewhat from my initial shock, I said, "This is so unexpected that I can't allow myself to take you with me at this moment. Let me go home alone. Then we will correspond, and we will see what we should do next."

She found my argument reasonable, and I flew to New York alone, still wondering about this strange incident and the way my Japanese friends had tried to accommodate me.

Our correspondence lasted about two months. In her last letter she revealed that, being the only daughter of an aged mother, she would be hesitant to leave Japan. Niko went on to suggest that, not having any family myself, I should come to Japan and live in her house as her husband. She would take care of her mother and be a wife to me.

After that our correspondence ended. I could not see myself living in Japan for the rest of my life.

This was not my only experience with women seeking "arranged" marriages. In 1972, while in Paris, I decided to call a Russian woman whose advertisement for a husband I had seen in New York.

Over the phone we made arrangements for me to have dinner with her. On the way to her home I went to a delicatessan to buy some food and wine. Then, riding on the Metro, I began examining my packages of food. To my surprise, all the packages bore pictures of the head of a dog. I realized then that I had bought dog food. I returned to the store and tried to explain, though I spoke no French, that I wanted food for human beings, not for dogs. The deli was kind enough to exchange the dog food for human food, and I continued on my way. Nevertheless, no romantic involvement materialized from that visit.

As the Apollo program came to a close, military contracts were also being canceled, and my company drastically curtailed its electronic activities. I decided to take early retirement and work in a new field. I had already been offered academic positions by two leading universities, and I was also considering work as an electronics expert for the United Nations. The latter possibility appealed strongly to my love of travel, and I was contemplating what steps I should take to secure U.N. employment when Providence took charge of the situation.

One afternoon as I sat at my desk, the telephone sounded with a particularly imperative ring. A woman from an international travel bureau in New York was calling to discuss a job she thought I might be interested in. The next day in her office, she explained the nature of the job. The agency had sought me out to explain "the Russian Soul" to a high-ranking person who would be taking a long assignment in Moscow.

"That person," the woman said, "has undertaken an intensive course in Russian literature. He reads Russian, but in his reading he frequently stumbles over the word 'soul,' not fully understanding its meaning." Would I agree for a very good price to give him a short course in the Russian Soul?

I laughed heartily and explained that I was an electronics engineer, specializing in microelectronics, and not a specialist in Russian Soul. She was not only unconvinced but she claimed that her company had definite information as to my comprehensive knowledge of the Russian Soul and that there was no point in my denying it. She persuaded me to take a chance, although I had not the faintest idea where to start. Obviously somebody had played a trick on me.

Back at home, it was clear that I must learn something about the Russian Soul. Reading Dostoevsky, Tolstoy, and other great Russian authors, I discovered many references to "the soul" that I hadn't noticed when I had read the books in my youth. Newly equipped with fresh knowledge of these works, I organized a chronology of Russia that focused on events involving "the Russian Soul," trying to interpret that mystical essence in a historical context. With a light heart, I began to teach my student "the Russian Soul" in a context that was quite simply a brief history of Russia. In a week the course was over, and everyone was happy, especially my student, who heaped praise upon the international travel company for its ability "to retrieve such an excellent specialist in Russian Soul."

The following week I went to the agency to get my well-deserved and unexpectedly large paycheck. Highly amused, I again told the woman who had hired me that I was not "a super-duper specialist" on the Russian Soul. "Then what *is* your specialty?" she asked me, apparently not recalling what I had told her during our interview.

"First give me my check," I said, "then I will repeat to you who I am."

When it finally dawned on her that I was indeed an engineer and specialist in microelectronics, she reached to the phone and called her husband, the chief of personnel at the United Nations. "Are you still looking for a microelectronics specialist?" she asked him.

"Yes," he replied. "Why do you ask?"

"That specialist is here at my desk!" she exclaimed.

Two weeks later I was on my way to India for my first U.N. assignment.

On the plane with Astronaut Neil Armstrong, on the way to Cape Canaveral, Florida.

At the wedding of my son, in San Diego, CA. From left to right—Dr. and Mrs. Milo Youel, Edward Jr. and his bride Bobby, Virginia and myself.

DI QVI MARCONI LANCIO
IL PRIMO SEGNALE RADIO
PRIMAVERA MDCCCXCV

Famous window in Marconi's villa, in Bologna, Italy, from which the world first radio signal was transmitted 101 years ago.

"The Shiek of Araby". as my friends called me, enjoying a camel ride near the Giza Pyramids.

In the desert, near the Pyramids, my students demonstrate the operation of a tape-recorder powered entirely by solar energy. A respectful reminder of my work in that field.

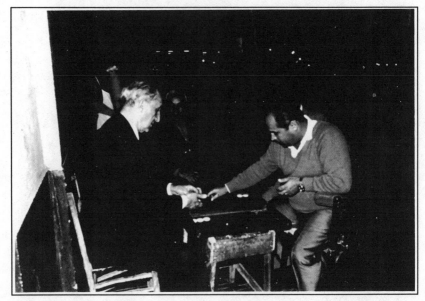

I am playing backgammon in the Khan-al-Khalili bazaar, in Cairo. Unexpectadly I won and was carried on shoulders of on-lookers with the chant: "Coca-Cola, Coca-Cola".

On a hot air balloon in New Mexico, in 1990.

NINE

*I*ndia again—the India of Rabindranath Tagore, the author of classic Indian novels, dramas, and books of philosophy. As a teenager in Tiflis, I had read in Russian translation one of his important works, *Sadhama: The Realization of Life,* written in 1913. The book dealt, as I recall, with social reform and international unity, and it was very critical of the Indian caste system that still, sadly, prevails in India.

As a teenager it was not easy to comprehend many of his ideas, since my Soviet environment was so different from India, but Tagore's commitment to social justice affected me deeply. This intellectual giant was born in 1861, lived his life, and wrote the world-famous works for which he received the well-deserved Novel Prize for Literature in 1913.

India was such fertile ground for new ideas. Mohandas Gandhi (1869-1948), the Indian political and spiritual leader, was not as well known to me as Tagore in my younger days. I did know that he drew much of his inspiration from the thinking of Leo Tolstoy on civil disobedience and nonviolent resistance to injustice, that he spent years in jail, and that he was shot and killed by an anarchist in 1948.

I had come under the spell of this fascinating country when I first visited it in 1960. Its beauty, its matchless colors (India is called the photographer's paradise), despite its unbelievable poverty from the Westerner's perspective, had lingered in my memory.

Unlike my previous trip to India, this one gave me the opportunity to stay much longer and observe the country in depth, thanks to my new position as a United Nations Expert inspecting Indian semiconductor facilities throughout the country. Coincidentally, the U.N. representative I reported to there happened to be a KGB colonel whom I had met accidentally years earlier in Leningrad.

Seeing me, he was flabbergasted. I did not have to mention to him that I was now an American. By joining the U.N., one automatically becomes "stateless" and one's allegiance is to the U.N., not to one's own country, as long as one remains a U.N. employee.

I submitted my credentials to my new boss. After that, I was fortunate enough to have no more dealings with him, since I was assigned for the rest of my stay to representatives of the Indian government. They provided me with all the conveniences I needed for my job: air travel, hotel, chauffeur-driven cars, and above all, warm hospitality in their homes.

With the wholehearted assistance of my Indian hosts, I was able to visit many places: Hyderabad, Bombay, Poona, Nadiad, Ghasiabad, Naraina, and others. Thus I had a unique opportunity to observe the people and their customs, the caste system, and other aspects of everyday life.

Originally there were four castes in India: the *Brahmans,* or priests; *kshatriyas,* nobles and warriors; *vaisyas,* traders; and *sudras,* serfs. Over many centuries the four castes split into thousands of subgroups based on occupation and geography.

Below the castes are tens of millions of "untouchables"— casteless people. Although "untouchability" has been outlawed in India, it is still enforced in the villages. The untouchables are not permitted to dress well, must live in wretched housing, and may not worship in Hindu temples.

Hindus make up 80 percent of the population. Despite the country's perennial food shortage, they do not eat meat. The cow is considered sacred.

In New Delhi I visited the home of Dr. Barucha. He and his attractive wife lived in a new government house on the outskirts of town. On the way to his home, I could not miss seeing the sacred cows, completely unattended, that wandered through the streets. They can approach vegetable stands and eat whatever they please, while the vendors not only refrain from chasing them away but observe them with happy smiles, delighted by the visit of such unexpected visitors. If the vendors lose every bit of their merchandise, it does not bother them at all. I observed such scenes in several Indian towns.

Monkeys in India share privileges similar to those of the sacred cows. I saw a group "visiting" a pottery shop in the middle of a town. Within five minutes the shop's entire display—glasses and pottery— had been thrown on the floor and broken by monkeys jumping from one shelf to another. Did the shop owner stop them? God forbid! They were sacred creatures, and their visit was a blessing.

Another day, several buses, including the one I was riding in, were held up on the road for more than 30 minutes. Monkeys, five of them, were crossing the road; at least that seems to have been their original intention. After reaching the middle of the road, however, some of them apparently changed their minds and returned to their starting point. Then they changed their minds again and went back to the middle of the road. Meanwhile, two more monkeys showed up from the other side of the road to join the group, while all traffic was at a standstill, patiently waiting for the monkeys to make up their minds and get off the road.

In India there are shoe-repair stands on the sidewalks. A customer stands up in front of the stand while his shoes are repaired, usually within 10 or 15 minutes. It's an efficient operation indeed.

The shoe-shine stands are a different matter, however. In any other country I have been in, the customer sits on a high chair while his shoes are shined by a man seated below, at the level of the shoes. In India it's the other way around. The shoe-shiner sits on an elevated chair while the customer stands on the street below him. To reach the customer's shoes, the shoe-shiner has to bend far, far down, in such an awkward position that just looking at him makes one dizzy.

Another unconventional scene I came across was the washing site where people wash their clothes along a canal. My first visual impression was of color—striking color everywhere. When I looked more closely, I saw to my surprise that, unlike the custom in other countries, here the washing of the clothes was being done by men. The strangest thing of all was that the men were standing in water up to their waists, scrubbing the clothes on the edge of the canal and rinsing them in the canal itself. Then the women spread them on bushes and on the ground for drying. This colorful panorama was an enchantment for photographers.

Dr. Barucha's house, where he lived with his wife and two daughters, was a two-story structure with two bedrooms on the second floor and the living room and kitchen on the first floor. It was a very conventional, simple, unpretentious, and moderately comfortable house, one of many built by the government for its employees in 1970 to ease the burden of the acute housing shortage so prevalent in all large Indian cities.

In front of the house was a stand on wheels. A woman was ironing various garments and bedding items on the stand, using an old-fashioned charcoal-heated iron. After finishing her work, she would move her stand in front of the next house. I found that this type of service is common in the cities, where housewives seldom do their own ironing.

There was a little girl, only one or two years old, sitting patiently on a board under the stand. She must have been the woman's daughter, traveling with her mother wherever there was work to be done. It was a pitiful sight.

My hosts served me a delightful meal. I don't remember what it was, but everything was tasty and the tea was aromatic. After dinner, about 10:00 p.m., my hosts took me back to my hotel. Strangely, despite the late hour, the streets were full of people walking, talking, buying, selling. In short, India's life was in full swing at a time when evening activities would be dying down in western cities (except perhaps Paris, London, New York, and other world capitals).

In front of my hotel, workers were repairing the road. I was amazed by their method. All the work was done manually. In small baskets on top of their heads, women carried stones and bricks to the men, who laid them out on the road. The loads the women carried were rather small, and they moved slowly and gracefully in their colorful saris. Yet the job, albeit slowly, was done perfectly! After the completion of one job, the workers would move to another location to do similar work.

Where did they live? Where did they sleep? Where did they eat? I could not find out. It seems that they are part of whatever location they are in, part of the scenery. They sleep on the bare ground and nourish themselves by cooking on a fire right by the side of the road.

In Bombay, however, I saw a picture I would never forget. Next to the city's beautiful high-rise buildings there was a mass of primitive tents and shacks where construction workers lived, slept, and died. The contrast between these two worlds—high-rises and shacks—was unbelievable. It reminded me of similar scenes in Hong Kong and other large Asian and Middle Eastern cities, except that here in Bombay, with its magnificent skyscrapers, the contrast was much, much more striking.

Also in Bombay I found a lonely Armenian Church of St. Peter, built in 1796, where services were held every Sunday even though there were no parishioners. There were only two women there, a mother and her daughter. The mother played the organ and the daughter sang to a completely empty church, keeping the tradition.

"What happened to all the parishioners?" I asked them.

"They all moved away," was the reply. "They all went to America. Nobody is left here any more." Yet the two women kept the church open every Sunday, just as if it were full of parishioners.

"If the authorities would close the church one day, we both would die," they said. "There would be nothing left for us to live for." Obviously the two women had been affected by Hindu spiritualism.

One day I was invited to the posh wedding of the daughter of a well-to-do industrialist.

"What does the groom do for a living?" I asked the bride's father.

"He is living," said he with pride.

I was puzzled by his answer and repeated my question, adding, "What is his profession?"

"I told you," the industrialist said. "He is living."

Then I understood what he meant: the young man was a playboy. Again I felt the shattering contrast between the rich ("living") people and the poor, whose living conditions are little better than those of animals. In fact, many thousands of sacred cows are better off than India's poor people.

I could not help but recall my previous trip to India and the encounter with a rich maharani who called the poor people "dogs."

Another day I met a man named Roa, who invited me for a "tiger hunt." At 6:00 in the morning, I began watching for the car that was to have picked me up. I waited for more than twelve hours, until finally, at 6:10 p.m., a taxi sent by Mr. Roa arrived. When we got to his house, he was loading his car to take me for the "tiger hunt." I carefully pointed out that it might be too late for such an expedition.

"Don't worry," Mr. Roa said. "Don't you see? The sun is still up."

It was, true enough, but only for a few more minutes, and soon the evening descended. "Yes," he said then. "You were right. It is somewhat late, but do not worry, we will go."

By 6:35 the little Indian car was finally packed. Besides Mr. Roa and me, there were his wife, his three children, a servant, and a little dog squeezed into the car.

It was pitch dark as we drove alongside a wooded area. As the car moved, the servant would indiscriminately discharge his gun from the open window toward the bushes. After every shot, he would let the dog run into the bushes, presumably to pick up the "wounded tiger." With the dog back in the car, we would happily continue our ride.

At about 8:00, the servant let the dog out and fired the gun. We heard the yelp of a wounded animal from the bushes.

"We got the tiger!" exclaimed Mr. Roa. "We got him!"

Minutes later we discovered that "the tiger" was our dog, which had been slightly wounded in the leg. We picked him up and the "tiger hunt" was pronounced over. It was declared that it was time for a picnic. We stopped the car on the roadside, and Mr. Roa took bed sheets from the trunk, spreading them right smack in the middle of the road because it provided the necessary flat surface.

His wife had just finished putting the dishes out when a car appeared, the driver blasting the horn for us to let him pass by. All the Roas were genuinely surprised. "Why should a strange car use this road when we are about to have our picnic?" they asked.

We had no choice, however, than to pick up the dishes and pull the tablecloth to the side so that the car could pass. After the car had gone by, the tablecloth was again spread upon the road and the dishes were arranged on it. "It's okay," Mr. Roa assured me. "Nobody should come in this direction again tonight." No sooner had he said this but another car appeared, and the entire procedure was repeated. It was already 10:30 and we were all very hungry. We decided not to have a picnic after all and to go home for supper.

There was a charcoal-burning stove in the Roas' kitchen. Rain-soaked charcoal was brought in from outdoors, and Mr. Roa used three packs of matches trying to light it. He finally gave up trying to set fire to wet charcoal. "You are right again," he said composedly. "We should have kept at least some of the charcoal in a dry place." Unable to start a fire, we had to be satisfied with cold cuts and some fruit.

At 1:00 a.m., about to leave for my hotel, I passed through the kitchen of Mr. Roa's relatively new house and noticed that the water faucet above the kitchen sink had been placed just beneath the level of the ceiling!

"It is done so children can't reach it," my host explained.

"Then how do *you* use it?" I asked.

"It's very simple," he said. "We use a ladder."

"What do you do when you need to wash your dishes?" I persisted.

"It's very simple," he said again. "For that occasion we attach a narrow cloth ribbon to the faucet so that the water can run into the sink without splashing around."

The car was waiting, so I thanked my most pleasant hosts for providing me with such an unforgettable experience.

Skilled labor in India is not readily available. The scientists and engineers, however, are very well versed in their fields. Still, the lack of adequate facilities hampers their effectiveness. In my particular specialty, semiconductors, they have made considerable progress, introducing new products and erecting new factories and laboratories; but in the construction of such facilities they have failed to introduce modern planning. In some semiconductor factories I observed how workers would tear down just-completed building walls because no one had remembered to allow for installation of the heating system and gas pipes. Having remedied that oversight, they then discovered that they had forgotten to include telephone and electric wires. Down would come the wall again. The process was repeated when the builders realized they had failed to install the prescribed pipes for air and ventilation so essential in semiconductor manufacturing.

Such delays go on and on until eventually the building is finished. But what a waste of time and energy! Endless "modifications" and the fact that everything is done manually prolong the building's completion considerably. No one minds, however, because labor is cheap and they have lots of time.

Once I stayed overnight in the guest house of an ultramodern factory where transistor radios were manufactured. One end of the long factory building was designated for drying white onions and packaging them to be shipped abroad. There was a long assembly line where from fifty to seventy women were pilling and cutting the onions, which were fed on a huge conveyor into a drying oven. The onion smell was unbearable, but the women were apparently used to it, and while I was able to stay there for less than two minutes, the women's eyes never burned during their eight-hour shifts.

The proceeds from the export of the dried onions were used to purchase transistors abroad. The transistors were shipped back to the same plant, and an assembly line opposite where the onions were processed was used for manufacturing portable transistor radios. Thus one can say, jokingly, that they were making radios out of dry onions within the same building!

The factory's large guest room, where I stayed overnight, had a single bed in the middle, a toilet in the corner, and, next to the bed, a shower with no curtain and no drain. Water splashed on the bed and collected on the floor. "Don't worry," I was told. "In an hour all will be dry again."

In India there were many such surprises. On one occasion I visited a newly built transistor factory. Such a plant normally has a so-called "clean" or "white" room, where tightly controlled air circulation prevents contamination of the transistors during the manufacturing process. Any particle in the air, however microscopic, can ruin transistors. Knowing this, I was taken aback by the condition of this particular plant's "clean" room. There were cracks in the walls, windows, and door through which outside air freely entered.

"Where is your clean room?" I asked.

"This is it," the manager replied. "We just painted it white; can't you see?"

Such misunderstandings were prevalent only during the learning period, when India was just beginning to master the new technology. Now, I am told, the country's manufacturing standards are comparable to those in many industrialized countries.

However irrational, however contradictory, India will remain in my memory as an extraordinary country, with its street barbers, beggars, and holy men; sacred cows and monkeys roaming the streets; magnificent temples with ornate carved stone windows through which the sun could barely shine; gigantic posters depicting movies and favorite celebrities; women wearing colorful saris even while they carried stones and bricks on their heads or washed clothes; unmatched hospitality at any social level; strong family ties; respect for the elderly; the caste system; the multitude of religious sects; and many, many other features that make India unique. I was fortunate to learn first-hand about the place that has enriched me with wonderful memories.

When I think of India after so many years, I remember color—striking colors everywhere!

When my contract expired I returned to New York to receive my new U.N. assignment. This time it would be Egypt, where I would stay nearly three years.

Little did I know that my journey to Egypt would lead to a lifelong fascination with its archaeology. What did I know of Egypt? Not very much, except that it had been home to one of the principal civilizations of the ancient Middle East—indeed, of the entire ancient world.

The Great Pyramids of Gizza, only remaining structures among the Seven Wonders of the Ancient World? Yes, I had read a lot about them, looked at pictures, and never ceased to be puzzled about how they had been erected with such precision, on such a colossal scale. How could I have known that the day would come when I would be living only five miles from the great Cheops, the most breathtaking structure on earth, rising forty stories above the desert?

And what of Alexandria (in Arabic, *El Iskandriya*), the center of literature, ideas, scholarship, and science for nearly a thousand years after the death of its founder, Alexander the Great? The library of Alexandria had contained 500 thousand papyrus rolls in ancient times. Even the great mathematician Euclid worked there in 300 B.C.

And what of the mummification of the bodies of deceased pharaohs? What of the magnificent temples along the Nile, lifegiver to Egypt for many millenia? ("Egypt is the gift of the Nile," said the Greek historian Hecatalus.) I read about all these things and was thrilled to be entering that distant world, to be living there for three full years, not as a tourist but as a resident.

Egypt is older than any other Western civilization except perhaps Mesopotamia. With a history spanning six thousand years, it has been defined by the Nile River and shaped by outside conquerors including the Romans, Persians, Arabs, Turks, French, and British.

More than 1,300 years old, Cairo reigns at the head of the Nile Delta, 130 miles southeast of Alexandria. Its name comes from the Arabic *El Qahira,* which means "victorious city." The older part of the city has twisted, narrow streets lined with houses four or five stories high. Above the dirt and crowds on the streets rise the pink and brown minarets that ornament the mosques where Islamic worship takes place. It is said that the Mosque of Ahmed Ibn Tulun was built on the spot where God spoke to Moses.

When I arrived in Cairo I was met by my driver, Hakim, a dark-faced Nubian, driving a new Peugeot, which would be my U.N. car. He drove me to the accommodations that had been arranged for me. They looked like upgraded barracks, and I decided that I would rather find an apartment on my own. Meanwhile, I stayed in a house owned by an Englishwoman, the widow of an Egyptian colonel. The rooms were decorated with portraits of Soviet leaders, and Lenin's picture was in every room. Seeing this, I decided not to disclose that I was a former Soviet citizen who had spent almost half his life in the Soviet "paradise." As I expected, she freely described to me the happy life that people experienced in the Soviet Union, which she had never visited. She was enjoying this, apparently trying to brainwash me, and I listened to her fairy tales with restraint, never expressing my sentiments on the subject.

After a week, I found a villa near the middle of town and quickly moved my belongings there. The rent was high—$1,200 a month—expensive even by American standards, but I was unable to find any other convenient place in Cairo, which was suffering from an acute housing shortage.

When I tried to purchase insurance for theft protection, I found the premium exorbitant and soon learned that I could hire a guard to protect my villa 24 hours a day for just $12 a month. They call such people *bawabs* in Arabic ("gatekeepers"). The *bawab* is a very important person in Cairo's households. He becomes familiar with the most intimate likes and dislikes of the tenants he serves and represents one of the city's most enduring institutions.

My *bawab* Achmet was a Nubian from the dark-skinned ethnic group of southern Egypt and northern Sudan. The Nubians are considered to be most trustworthy servants and are valued for their reliability, dignity, and imposing height. My Achmet was at least six feet tall.

He lived at my villa's front door with his wife. They ate there and they slept there. My Achmet washed my car every morning, swept the floor in front of the villa, and helped carry heavy packages from the car. In short, he made my life in strange Cairo quite comfortable. (He was also the keeper of my landlady's purse, giving her money when she went shopping.)

When I quit my U.N. job and then returned to Egypt a second time to teach at Cairo University, I rented the same villa, and when I arrived there I was pleased to see my Achmet. He astonished me by handing me $140, money I had kept under the rug and had forgotten about when I checked out of the villa the previous year. He had found the money when he was cleaning the floor and had kept it to give me in case I would come back. Nothing like this could have happened any other place in the world!

My U.N. assignment in Egypt was as Director of Research and Development Facilities in the Electronic Systems Center, located about twenty miles south of Cairo. As the person responsible for overseeing the development of electronic measuring equipment, I soon found that the Center was engaged in an impossible task, that of duplicating foreign high-tech gears with totally unqualified personnel.

The Center's manager was a peppery individual, a very short man who wore three-inch platform shoes and sat behind his desk on a chair elevated five inches off the floor. He would not heed my advice to concentrate the Center's efforts on a more realistic goal, developing one or two basic gears rather than going in many different directions at the same time with the same limited and ineffective staff.

His logic, I discovered later, went something like this: "Who cares if we produce anything, as long as the U.N. is paying for it?" The more grandiose (however unrealistic) the program, the more money he would get from the U.N.

Following that logic, he had ordered nearly a hundred microfilms of electronics periodicals from the U.S., going back twenty or twenty-five years and paying an enormous sum. Obviously he had no intention of using them, since he "forgot" to get a microfilm reader for the films, which were buried in a storeroom.

In the same vein, a number of expensive but useless pieces of equipment had been ordered and lay unpacked for years. "Spend, spend, and spend" was the motto of the operation.

When I mentioned my misgivings about this strange practice to a fellow U.N. engineer, he replied, "Remember, you are valued not by your accomplishment but by the amount of money you can spend." It had a chilling effect on me and was so contrary to my entire way of thinking that after a year I resigned from the U.N. In the meantime, the only thing accomplished in the Center was that its manager succeeded in making enough money to build an expensive villa for himself in the city's choicest location. That is life.

During my time at the Electronic Center, I advertised for a secretary in the leading Egyptian newspaper, *El Ahram*. In my ad I specified knowledge of the English language as an important requirement. Six young women responded and came to my office for interviews, during which I dictated an English text and asked the applicants to write it down. Then I asked them to translate it to Arabic. Not knowing a single word of Arabic, I collected the translations and proceeded to ask other questions. One of the applicants, Abla El Heneidy, was especially fluent in English, having once lived in New York City, not to mention that she was the prettiest of the applicants. Jokingly I asked her whether she used the same pen for writing in English and Arabic. "Of course," she said seriously. "Why do I have to change my pen?"

"It is just amazing," I replied with equal seriousness. "I didn't realize that one pen could write in two different languages."

For a moment she was stunned. "I never thought about it," she said. Then, realizing that I was joking, she said, "I want to work for you no matter what my salary would be. Please hire me."

I did hire her, and not only was she an outstanding secretary, she became a good friend. She helped me both in the office and in everyday life in this strange foreign country, where the English language was not common as it had been in India.

In Egypt it is not unknown for secretaries to give roses to their bosses. One day Abla took me to a flower stand to buy me roses; it was the anniversary of my arrival in Egypt. After selecting two dozen long-stemmed roses, she asked the price.

"Four dollars," said the merchant.

"It's too much!" Abla exclaimed. "How about fifty cents?"

From that point, they began typical Egyptian bargaining. The merchant would reduce his price by ten cents, and Abla would respond with a five-cent increase in her offer. The whole process took at least twenty minutes. In the end the parties compromised on seventy-five cents. When she handed the money to the merchant, I noticed that she paid not seventy-five cents but a dollar and seventy-five cents.

"What was the extra dollar for?" I asked.

"It was my tip to him," Abla said, "for bargaining so well."

The best word for traffic in Cairo is "indescribable," but I will try to describe it anyway. Automobiles, camels, trucks, pedestrians, trolleys, bicycles, and pushcarts all move at the same time and often not in the same direction. One must see this mess to believe it! Since telephone service is at best intermittent, many of the drivers who clog the roads are there because they are unable to reach the other party on the phone.

My telephone in the villa was often dead, forcing me to call a repairman and tipping him each time. As usual, he would blame the problem on faulty wiring, which he would quickly fix by climbing on the roof. When this repair ritual became too frequent (occurring at least twice a week), I became suspicious. One day, when I had again lost my telephone service, I climbed on the roof myself to see what had happened. The wires of my telephone had simply been disconnected! My Achmet explained matter-of-factly that the disconnecting had been my repairman's doing, a way of securing weekly tips.

The next time the repairman came, I not only refused to give him a tip but put my fist close, very close to his face and told him that I would not hesitate to "fix" his face in my way. He got the message, and my telephone had no further problems, at least on my end of the line.

I faced a similar problem with mail. I received no mail over a period of two months, though I knew that my son and my friends from the States would have been writing to me. I asked my Achmet what the problem might be.

"Have you paid your mailman a good tip?" he asked.

"No," I replied. "I did not know that the mailman should be paid for delivering the mail." Apparently, however, that was the custom in Egypt. The next time I saw the mailman, I handed him a dollar without saying a word. In return he gave me fourteen undelivered letters.

Nearly every foreigner is affected at one time or another by diarrhea. I decided to face the problem directly. Knowing that I would be there for a long time and that I couldn't always watch what I ate and drank, I decided to develop an immunity right from the start. The first two days of my stay, I forced myself to eat fruits and vegetables right in the bazaars and drink unboiled water. Sure enough, on the third day I was struck, as I had expected, with the worst case of diarrhea imaginable. After four days, lying helplessly in bed, in a strange environment, without knowing how to communicate with those around me, I fell into a coma. But my body, used to suffering from my days in Leningrad and the German camps, withstood the test, and on the sixth day I recovered, to the surprise of those around me. I had succeeded in becoming immune, and from then on I was able to eat anything, anywhere in Egypt, with no adverse consequences; but I don't recommend following my example.

My U.N. car and its assigned chauffeur were always ready to take me wherever I wanted to go. Soon I became uncomfortable with his being attached to me day and night; it felt like an intrusion on my privacy. So I decided to release him for good and drive the car myself.

My U.N. associates could not believe that I could drive my car in Cairo's chaotic traffic without a driver who knew his way around and could rescue me in case of an accident. But I was determined to try. First I went to the Egyptian motor vehicle bureau to pass my driver's examination. Then it was time to get the driving certificate, a process that turned out to be the adventure of "a thousand and one nights."

The bureau sent me to the other side of town to buy a "special paper" (simply a plain sheet of eight-by-ten-inch typing paper) and bring it back for the actual typing of my certificate. Then they sent me to another part of Cairo to obtain a signature from an official. Then I had to go back to the bureau to get the certificate stamped. At that point an official told me that I needed other stamps attached to my certificate, stamps I could obtain only in yet another part of the city. I went and got those, too.

But my adventures were not over yet. After spending four days running back and forth to various locations in Cairo, I found myself once again standing in front of the same official, who stared at my paper and said, "You are missing one more signature. If you wait, I'll get it for you."

He disappeared into another room, returning with the papers of other applicants but not mine. When, after waiting for two hours, I shouted at him, asking what was going on and why I was not getting my papers, he said that the other man was asking five dollars to affix his signature. I saw that I had no choice but to give the official five dollars for the "other man," and I finally obtained that hard-won piece of paper and rushed out of the place.

Counting all the money I paid for the paper, the stamps, and the signatures, my driver's license cost me just forty-five dollars, which may have been reasonable for the bribes if not for the four-and-a-half days of frustration I had been through. Now equipped with an Egyptian driver's license (which, incidentally, I never once had to show to any traffic cop), I said a final goodbye to my driver and got behind the wheel. My driver could not believe that I would dare drive the car without him. But I did, during my entire stay in Egypt, and had not a single accident nor put a single scratch on my brand-new bright, white Peugeot. I should admit, however, that it may have been partly because of the pack of American cigarettes I always kept on my dashboard for traffic cops, who would clear my way immediately through the traffic, even sometimes reversing the direction of the traffic to let me through.

Yes, I had to learn my way in Egypt.

Once, on my way to visit a friend in the outskirts of the city, I got lost. At an intersection I asked for directions from the policeman regulating the traffic from his position in an elevated booth at least ten feet above street level. I was unable to understand his explanation and, seeing this, he stepped down from the booth, placed himself next to me in the car, and directed me to my friend's house two-and-a-half miles away. When I tried to pay for this unexpected service, he said, "Give me only fifty cents for a taxi to get back to my booth." I gave him a dollar and he kissed me on my cheek and disappeared. I could imagine what a traffic jam he must have found after being away nearly twenty-five minutes.

On another occasion, when I was driving slowly near the University, an elderly man tried to throw himself under my car. I was unable to avoid him, so I stopped the car. He was screaming loudly, although I was sure I had not run over him, stopping just in time. Hearing his screams, people started to gather around. Being a foreigner, I thought that it would be best for me to avoid the crowd and take my "victim" to the nearest hospital. But on the way to the hospital, he pleaded with me to take him home instead. I agreed, and upon arriving home, he walked away as if nothing had happened.

Later, relating this episode to my Egyptian friends, they told me that the man had simply wanted a free ride home.

After I left my U.N. job and returned to New York, I received a grant from the U.S. National Science Foundation to become a Visiting Professor at Cairo University, a state institution with 55,000 students and teaching personnel. The university has very few foreign professors, and most teaching is in Arabic. (Cairo University should not be confused with the private American University of Cairo, where teaching is only in English.)

Egypt has other large universities as well. Al-Azhar University, located in the Al-Azhar Mosque in Cairo's medieval quarter, has been a teaching center for the entire Muslim world for more than a thousand years. There are also universities in Ayn Shams and Asyut as well as other institutions of higher learning throughout the country.

Higher education in the state universities is free for men and women. Thus Egypt has more university graduates per capita than any other country in the world. Unfortunately, a majority of the graduates have no chance of being employed in their own country because so few positions are available, so they are drifting to other Arabic-speaking countries such as Saudi Arabia, Kuwait, and Syria. Thus Egypt spends millions of dollars to educate and train young people not for its own improvement but for the benefit of other countries, which makes little sense to me.

A third of the students are girls. Although their chances of employment are practically nil, a university diploma gives them a better chance of marrying. It has almost become a status symbol for even the most poorly educated men to choose a wife with higher education. And what do the girls do with their diplomas once married? The diplomas almost always end up in the wastepaper basket. It is another example of a tremendous waste of national resources. There are exceptions, but they do not change the larger picture.

The university's classrooms where I began my teaching were dimly lit, and the laboratories were a chaotic mixture of new and out-dated equipment. Yet the students worked diligently, and I was pleased to see how seriously they took their responsibilities.

The library was a large depository of very old texts, along with some new ones. The librarian was considered a very important person. In her absence, none of the two dozen or so assistant librarians could make any decisions about matters such as the purchasing of books or making photocopies of texts.

One day I found the library closed. It remained closed for six days, leaving students with no service. I was told that the librarian was spending time with her sister, who was visiting from out of town.

"So why is the library closed?" I asked, annoyed. I was told that only the librarian had a key. I found it amazing that the librarian would not trust the key to one of her many library assistants.

An equally foolish and more wasteful practice in government

institutions is that of secretaries having the company of several other females when typing or taking dictation, the "company" being paid as much as the secretary just for being present.

I found the teaching personnel autocratic, having very limited contact with the students except in the classroom, where the professor could read his lecture for forty-five minutes without interruption. Students had to write everything down in minute detail and never interrupt their notetaking by raising their hands, since the professor would require the exact wording of his lecture to be reproduced on the examination. Any deviation or interpretation would generally result in the student flunking.

Being used to the more open American practice, I completely violated this Egyptian tradition, encouraging my students to interrupt me with questions. However, I got the shock of my life after two or three months, when I asked one of my students how my lectures were being received.

"Not very well," was her answer.

"Why?" I asked, intrigued.

"Because," she continued, "when you speak it's so easy to understand; it's so clear."

"What's wrong with that?" I exclaimed.

"We expected you, a prominent professor from the U.S., to speak over our heads so that we would not understand," she said. "Now do you see why we are disappointed in you?"

Another violation: I socialized with my students to their delight, taking part in their picnics, visiting their homes, and meeting their parents. I established a cordial and personal relationship with them, to the dismay of my Egyptian faculty colleagues.

One day I was taken to the home of one of my students who lived in El Fayyum, thirty miles south of Cairo. The father was a photographer, and he took pictures of my visit with them. It was a joyful day for me in this warm family.

I also attended two weddings, both of female students of mine. At Egyptian weddings the bride and groom are seated on a high throne and surrounded by many flowers and children. While the guests engage in a food orgy, the couple must remain on the throne. At the weddings I went to, they sat for more than four hours without moving until the guests had finished eating. Then they were allowed to eat. A belly dancer was brought to the couple, to sit by them and photograph them. At one of the weddings it was my "responsibility" to escort the belly dancer to the bride and groom.

I found that Egyptians are great procrastinators. The attitude "why do today when there is tomorrow?" is called *boukra*, the Egyptian equivalent of the Spanish *mañana*. Another unique expression is *malish*, which translates roughly as "why cry over spilled milk?" *Malish* is used after car accidents, fires, even deaths. *In sha Allah* ("if God is willing") is another common expression. If you put the initial letters of those three words together, you will get "IBM," the name of the most popular company in Egypt.

Sometimes my students' papers would be turned in to me completely blank. When I would ask why, the student would reply, "Allah told me not to do it today; I could not disobey his order." That seemed to be a convenient excuse for avoiding responsibility or breaking promises. When one would ask an Egyptian to do a certain thing or be somewhere at a certain hour, he would always readily agree, adding, "*In sha Allah*,", giving him a way out if he changes his mind.

Such an attitude, in my opinion, contributes to progress being marginal in Egypt. It reflects the deep conservatism that dates back to the beginning of civilization, clinging to traditions of ancient generations. "Egypt is here to stay as it is," said one of my students.

The word "Islam" means "submission" (that is, to the will of God) in Arabic, and Muslims are "those who submit." Muslims express their belief in one god in the official confession of faith, the Shahada: "*La ilaha illa Allah, wa Muhammadun rasulu Allu*" ("there is no god but Allah, and Mohammed is his messenger"). Allah rewards the good and punishes the sinful, according to Islamic belief, and the victory of Israel over the Arab forces in 1967 was taken by many Muslims as a punishment from Allah for their failure to heed his prophets. Large numbers of Muslims returned to the orthodox tradition in response to this admonishment.

Fasting during the month of Ramadan, the ninth month of the Islamic calendar, is strictly observed. During Ramadan, people do not eat anything all day. After sundown, when the mullah chants the last prayer of the day, everybody rushes to eat, be it at home or in a public place, in the bazaars and restaurants. At that time the meal becomes a big feast.

Muslim tradition and worship are less conspicuous in Alexandria than in Cairo. Alexandria was long the center of Greek civilization and learning. For many centuries it was a center of commerce between the East and West and may once have had a population of as many as a million.

Two or three times I drove to Alexandria. The splendor of ancient and Byzantine times is gone. Now Alexandria looks like a poor orphan, with its dilapidated buildings, dirty streets, and makeshift shops. Only in the summer does it become vibrant, for it is a popular summer resort for Cairo inhabitants who want to escape from the city's scorching heat. In summertime the seashore at Alexandria is jammed with tents, looking like a gigantic ant colony, with a multitude of umbrellas so close to each other that they form a solid, multicolored carpet for five or six miles along the water. On the way from Alexandria to Tripoli in Libya, one can observe many brand-new automobiles abandoned because of the complete absence of any service on the road.

Halfway between Cairo and Alexandria is a popular rest area that welcomes travelers with a restaurant and gas station. At this point one can turn westward and enter the Western Desert. After driving for an hour, one comes to Wadie Natrun, where ancient monasteries are scattered in the desert. Some of these primitive structures date back as far as the fourth and fifth centuries A.D. There are only ten or fifteen Christian Coptic monks living in each monastery.

I found the monks well educated and civil, although they live in complete isolation from the world and sustain themselves with nearby vegetation and the meager crops they raise behind the monasteries' mud walls. I spotted two or three skinny goats that probably provided the entire milk supply.

The thick mud walls around the monasteries are a reminder that for centuries the monks had to protect themselves from attacks by Bedouins and other nomads. I saw no sign of defense weaponry, however. "Our weapons are our prayers," one of the monks said in very good English. All the monks spoke English, as well as Arabic and Coptic, the language of the ancient Egyptians. Coptic today is used exclusively as a liturgical language in the Coptic Orthodox Christian Church.

According to the latest census, Copts—the direct descendants of ancient Egyptians—constitute only ten percent of the entire Egyptian population. They have their own pope, who resides in Cairo, and their own cathedral, which I attended at Christmastime. During the service I observed an entire procession of people dressed as apostles, Wise Men, and others from the Christmas story who looked as if they had stepped right out of the pages of the Bible. It was an extraordinary sight.

Once, when I was crossing the Western Desert in my Peugeot on a clear and perfect day, I became trapped in a sandstorm. In less than fifteen seconds my car was completely buried. I had only a few seconds to get out of the car, but I remained nearby so that I wouldn't lose it as it disappeared under the sand. In two minutes or so the storm was just a memory. I didn't dare move, fearing that I would never see my car again and hoping that some help would arrive. Luckily, six Bedouins soon showed up. I tried explaining to them what had happened, pointing at the place where my car was buried. They found the car and attached ropes to different parts of it, then began to pull in six different directions at once. I was afraid that, instead of rescuing it, they would break the car apart. With considerable difficulty I persuaded them to pull in one direction only. When my car emerged from the sand, to my great surprise I was able to start it. When I asked how much I owed them for their labor, the leader of the Bedouins named a price of a hundred dollars. Even if I had been carrying such a sum, I would never have paid that amount. I offered them a dollar instead. They vigorously protested. Then I added another dollar and we sealed the transaction with a firm handshake.

Taxis in Egypt, especially in Cairo, are numerous, driven mostly by graduate students. For many it is the only job they can find after leaving the universities. A large number of policemen stand at the entrances to the big hotels and public places, noting the license plates of arriving and departing vehicles. Perhaps because of this practice, if one forgets an article in a taxi—which actually happened to me on one occasion—it is returned within twelve hours.

Aswan is a picturesque town on the Nile, about three hundred miles south of Cairo. Nearby cataracts and graceful *feluccas* (ancient crewed sailboats) moving smoothly on the waters of the Nile create a most pleasing picture well worth the brush of a painter. Aswan has the world's most equable climate, which is why many world leaders (Tito, Aga Khan, Churchill, and others) have had their hideaways there.

In 1975 there was a food riot in Cairo. I felt that it would be unsafe to stay in town, not knowing whether the angry crowd might turn on foreigners. I took the first flight to Aswan and checked in at the three-hundred-room Old Cataract Hotel, where I was the only guest. This hotel is an oasis of old-world elegance that sits high above the Nile waters. It takes its name from the first six cataracts (or rapids), which hindered early exploration of the Nile.

The next morning, when I was ready to shave, I discovered that there was no electricity in town. I located some telephone wires near the hotel switchboard, arranged them to get just enough juice to operate my shaver, and completed my shaving as the switchboard operator watched in stunned silence. I am sure the girl would remember for a long time how an American shaved his face using wires at her switchboard.

On another occasion I traveled to the famous Aswan High Dam completed by the Soviet government in 1970. It was a huge dam by any standards, and it had created the enormous Lake Nasser, three hundred miles long. There were twelve turbines with the potential capacity to generate two million kilowatts. Because of faulty design, however, the turbine blades quickly cracked and the power plant has never produced at capacity. In 1982, the U.S. gave the Egyptian government 85 million dollars to replace the blades.

The most disastrous consequence of the construction of the dam, however, was that it obstructed most of the valuable sediment, which is now retained in Lake Nasser, and forced the Nile to flood thousands of acres of the most fertile soil that once gave up two or three crops a year. The valuable deposition of silt was gone. Thousands and thousands of farmers lost their farmland and moved into Cairo and other urban areas, living on the streets in primitive tents. The government was now forced to purchase close to a billion dollars in fertilizers to compensate for the loss of valuable silt. Fertilizers became a huge and constant drain on the Egyptian economy in a country that had never needed any in the past.

Lake Nasser loses 350 billion cubic feet of water through evaporation. This affects the ecology and climate of the south of Egypt and Nubia. The evaporation of the lake makes its water more saline, adding to the salt problem in the Egyptian fields downstream. Daniel J. Stanly of the Smithsonian Institution predicts that the Egyptian Mediterranean coastline of the Nile Delta could move as much as twenty miles inland by the year 2100 because sediment once carried down the Nile, replacing coastal soil, is gone. More than a million people living in the area will be affected, and Alexandria will eventually be surrounded by the waters of the Mediterranean Sea. (This information appeared in *National Geographic*, May 1985 and February 1992.)

It became a standard joke among foreigners that the best way to help Egypt's economy would be to "blow up" the Aswan Dam. But Egyptians do not like to hear this because, in the minds of the masses, the gigantic dam remains a matter of false pride.

There was an unfinished bridge over the Nile, Ramses Bridge, which ended abruptly at the water's edge. There was no warning sign at the approaches to the bridge, and unwary motorists heading for the bridge often ended up in the waters of the Nile.

In Cairo I joined the Gazira Sports Club and swam frequently in its Olympic swimming pool. One day I heard a voice behind me saying, in Russian, "The way you swim, I can tell that you learned to do it in Russia." Turning, I saw a typical Russian face. We got out of the water and he introduced himself as a correspondent of the Soviet daily newspaper *Pravda*. Jokingly, I said, "You must be working for the KGB, because their agents always call themselves 'correspondents.'" He did not get angry, telling me that I was wrong and that he could prove that he was who he claimed to be. I asked him to show me some of his dispatches to *Pravda* under his own name. He readily agreed and invited me to come for dinner at his house.

On the agreed-upon day, I drove to his luxurious villa in Zamalek, an island in the middle of the Nile and an affluent sector of Cairo. I notified the local police in advance where I would be at what time, just in case something happened to me. The party at the correspondent's house was attended by several high-ranking KGB officials and their very attractive wives, who wore expensive jewelry. They had come to see "the Russian-speaking American," uncommon in their experience.

The host showed, as promised, his dispatches to prove that he was indeed an accredited correspondent, although that would not exclude his being a KGB agent as well. I discovered that he was a graduate of Cairo University and had been in Cairo for more than ten years. He was also a noted "Arabist" and knew the Arabic language better than most Arabs in Egypt. I took my hat off to the KGB, seeing how thoroughly they were preparing their agents who served abroad. Do we do the same when we send our officials and agents abroad unable to utter a word in the language of the country they are assigned to?

Our conversation soon shifted to life in America. I knew that as soon as I began to describe the positive aspects of America, the typical Soviet cliches would begin: terrible unemployment, exploitation of the working class, lynching of African Americans (my Soviet friends not only believed that this was still occurring but showed me current Soviet literature on the subject).

I quickly decided to turn the tables and began criticizing many aspects of life in the U.S., going so far as to complain that our credit-card system is a fraud because "in less than two months you have to pay to balance your account." I was also "indignant" about our public transportation systems, which require one to wait almost an entire minute before boarding a bus, and about how unfair it is to customers when stores refuse to take back merchandise after two years unless you produce the receipt, and so on, and on.

"I am sure," I concluded, "that nothing like this would be possible in your country, which is so perfectly centralized and operates to the full satisfaction of all its people."

This was too much for my listeners. One of them angrily shot back, "Do not fool yourself. We also have our problems, which you would not like at all." I expressed disbelief, they started arguing bitterly with one another, and soon after I left the villa.

During the U.S. Bicentennial Celebration, our embassy threw an elaborate party for nearly 140 foreign ambassadors in Egypt, members of their staffs, and Egyptian guests. Even Idi Amin was there. Our ambassador, who knew my Russian background, introduced me to the Soviet ambassador, a short, stocky man with heavy mustaches. The two of us conversed briefly in English. I noticed that he had some difficulty with English, and so, trying to accommodate him, I asked if it would be easier for him to speak in Russian. He was delighted and tried to find out how, as an American, I knew Russian so well. I was elusive. Later I told him that I had noticed a few mistakes in his Russian. He was even more amazed but agreed with me.

"Of course," he said. "You are right. Russian is not my native tongue."

"Then what is your native tongue?" I asked him.

"Armenian," he said, "although you, as an American, probably never heard of it."

"Could you please ask me some questions in Armenian?" I ventured. "I want to hear what it sounds like."

He spoke then in Armenian, and when I replied in perfect Armenian he almost exploded. He heartily embraced me and kissed me on the cheek, saying that he was so delighted to hear me speak Armenian that he would give a reception in my honor at the embassy the following Sunday.

Two days before the day for which the reception was planned, I accidentally met the ambassador on the street. I greeted him, but he passed by me as if he had never seen me before. Obviously the KGB had not been sleeping. I never saw him again.

Cairo is at its most exciting in the late evening hours after the heat of the day subsides. Traffic resumes its pace, the shops reopen, the bazaars are buzzing. At Khan-al-Khalili Bazaar, the air is redolent with the heavy scent of sandalwood and people haggle for every item they want to buy. Cafes along the Nile are full to capacity with people ordering beer and ice cream. Everybody, from the very young to the very old, is out. Life goes on in this way until the wee hours of the morning. Only business and government offices are closed at night.

Late one evening, in a dry-cleaning store, I was picking up a suit when a tall, very good-looking lady who had been standing behind me said in perfect English, "How come they want to charge me two dollars to clean my husband's suit when I noticed that you paid only seventy-five cents for yours?"

I replied that I could not help her, that perhaps it was because I was an old customer, I did not know. I ventured that if two dollars was too much for her she might try a much less expensive cleaner in the neighborhood where I lived. I gave her the address and was about to explain how to get there when she said, "You'd better tell it to my husband, who is sitting in the car."

I did, and suggested that he follow my car. It was just past midnight when we reached the shop, which unfortunately had already closed. Because they had driven so far, I invited them to stop for a cup of coffee at my place, to compensate them for their lost time. After a little hesitation they agreed. On the bookcase in my villa they noticed a Russian-Arabic dictionary and expressed their surprise.

"Do you study Russian from Arabic or Arabic from Russian?" they wondered.

When I told them my identity, they immediately switched from English to Russian and we continued to chat pleasantly until morning, forgetting the time. He was the Soviet consul in charge of issuing passports, and his wife was a teacher of English at the embassy school for children. Both were from Tashkent, Usbekistan—another of my incredible coincidences.

Knowing that the Usbeks are famous for an elaborate rice *pilaf*, I told them how much I would enjoy eating some. It was an obvious hint to be invited to their home, but I was not sure that he, as a high Soviet official, would dare to play host to an American. I was wrong, and two days later I was eating a most delectable *pilaf* using my fingers in the Usbek tradition instead of a spoon.

Before we began our meal, I half-jokingly asked if I could inspect the room for hidden microphones. They were not surprised at all and gave permission. I found none.

A few days later I went again to visit them. This time the door was closed and bore a note saying that the occupants had left permanently—another KGB "interference."

My son Karik was living in Chicago, and I wanted him to come to Egypt where I could introduce him to some pretty girls of Armenian descent, hoping to get him married. I sent him an airline ticket, and soon he was in Cairo. Two weeks after his arrival I gave a party at my villa with the help of my always helpful secretary, Abla. I provided my son with a "bouquet" of five of the most attractive girls there, along with their mothers. One of the mothers was the daughter of the late Yugoslav Regent Paul, Princess Elizabeth. She was there with her daughter (the future actress Catherine Oxenburg). The two were vacationing in Egypt, and I had met them on a long Nile trip to Abbu-Simbel, stopping along the way at various ancient temples.

Abbu-Simbel was built in 1270 B.C. by Ramses II in his own honor, along with another, smaller temple dedicated to his queen, Nefertari. A trip on the Nile River is a journey along Egypt's ancient lifeline and presents the awe-inspiring temples of Luxor, Karnak, and Kom Ombo as a reminder of the meaning of the word "monumental."

My son finally "zeroed in" on one of the girls, who agreed to meet him the next day at a restaurant. Karik was rather disappointed when the girl showed up with her mother as a chaperone. After exchanging some banalities, my son made one more attempt to date the girl. Again she came with her mother. Karik gave up, not realizing that it is the tradition of the Middle East for a girl to bring her mother along on a date; so he went home to Chicago as he had arrived, a bachelor.

While in Alexandria with Karik, we saw a monument to Nubar Pasha, an Armenian who distinguished himself as a minister of commerce and assumed an Egyptian name.

I have to mention the world-renowned Egyptian National Museum in Cairo, the depository of fascinating artifacts of ancient history and civilization in Egypt. The collections represent an amazing treasure trove of Egyptian antiquity, arts, and artifacts of spectacular beauty. My stay in Egypt made me an enthusiastic amateur Egyptologist, and upon returning to New York I joined the American Institute of Archaeology (AIA) as an active member of its branch in Long Island, New York.

During all my time in Egypt, the meat I ate did not seem to be any different from what I was accustomed to in the U.S. I thought I was eating beef, and only toward the end of my stay did I discover that I had been eating camel meat all along. There was no difference in taste.

One of the things I remember most fondly from Egypt is the wonderfully delicious bread. It is sold on every street corner, and it is placed directly on the sidewalk, with nothing between it and the ground.

My cook used to prepare dinner as if I had a family of ten and take the leftovers home to his family. His excuse was that he had worked for an ambassador who had a large family, and that was the way he was used to cooking. I soon put a stop to this practice.

Living alone with no family in a strange country, unable to speak the language, is no picnic, so I was glad to find a small Armenian community in Cairo. Numbering about three thousand, the community was old and, by Egyptian standards, prosperous. Many were in the jewelry business and lived in Helliapolis, a Cairo suburb about twenty miles south of the city. It was strange to me that they would not associate with Egyptians, living entirely to themselves in a sort of ghetto. Even at large social events, such as an Armenian Red Cross banquet where more than a thousand were present, I did not see a single Egyptian. Nevertheless, every time I attended a gathering I would take my secretary, Abla, with me, disregarding the disapproving hiss around me.

At the university I was paid in Egyptian pounds. On the first day of every month I would go to the bank to receive my salary. One day an old, poorly dressed man on line in front of me was receiving a huge amount of money from the teller. He stacked the money in his open basket, which soon overflowed. Then something extraordinary happened. With no attempt to cover the basket, he walked out to the street, carrying his money in full view of the pedestrians. Nothing like this could happen anywhere else, especially in urban areas. There are few burglaries in Egypt, primarily because the punishment is very severe.

My salary was on a par with that of university professors in the U.S., although the cost of living in Egypt was relatively low. Thus I accumulated a fairly large amount of Egyptian pounds, upon which I had to pay tax in U.S. dollars. It caused a serious dilemma for me, since the Egyptian banks would not convert Egyptian pounds into American dollars. What should I do? Fortunately, one of my Armenian friends, who had a hardware store in the center of Tahla Market, pointed to one of the beggars in the square and said the man could help me with my problem. He gave my address to the beggar, who showed up at my place two days later. He asked me how many Egyptian pounds I would like to exchange. Then he unbuttoned his miserable-looking *halabia* (a traditional Egyptian coat). I could not believe what I saw. Inside his coat there were packs and packs of American dollars hanging from various parts of the lining. Meticulously he took off the packs, cautiously counted the money, and handed it to me. In the same fashion he would take the Egyptian pounds, count them carefully, and put them in his huge pockets. It did not occur to me that the dollars might be counterfeit, since my Armenian friend had told me that such a possibility is excluded in that type of transaction. Naturally the exchange rate was less favorable to me than the official rate, but I did not care. Now I could pay my U.S. taxes in dollars.

When I wanted to sell my car, I placed an ad in the newspaper. A woman and her young daughter came to buy it and, without any attempt to bargain as is the Middle Eastern custom, she paid the full amount in cash. They were just about to leave when the woman asked me casually, "Have you ever given your car to any Egyptian to drive?"

"Not really," I said. "Only once or twice I have asked one of my Egyptian friends to drive it for me when I found myself in unfamiliar surroundings. Otherwise, I was the sole driver of my car."

Hearing this, she turned back to me and requested the return of her money. She said, "I would never buy a car if it had been driven by an Egyptian, even for a minute." Obviously Egyptian drivers did not enjoy a particularly favorable reputation.

When the time came for my departure from Egypt, it was clear that Abla would join the ranks of her unemployed compatriots with little chance of finding a good employment again. To help her, I made arrangements with an Arabic-English oil company for her to work there with my highest recommendation. On my last day in Egypt I took her to her would-be employer's office and asked her to go to the second floor to sign the necessary papers while I waited in the car. She barely entered the building, then quickly returned, saying, "The elevator does not work."

"Why didn't you take the stairs?" I asked, baffled.

"I could not do it," she answered, "because Allah stopped the elevator to tell me that I should not take that job." I was speechless.

That night at the Cairo Hilton Hotel I was introduced to an attractive American woman who was vacationing in Egypt with her fiance. The next day I sent her a dozen roses with my good wishes. I soon forgot the episode.

Twenty years passed, and once when I was with my present wife, Maria, in Santa Fe, New Mexico, a middle-aged lady approached me and said, "I was touched by the beautiful roses you sent me in Egypt twenty years ago. May I invite you for dinner tonight?"

As we dined, I asked her what had happened to her fiance. "We split shortly after we returned to America," she said. If only I had known at the time.

My prolonged visits to India and Egypt have enriched me enormously. The memories are cherished, the friends are vivid and warm in my thoughts, the experiences are prized for their contribution to my understanding. Although people behave differently the world over, with different customs and practices and lifestyles, their similarities are striking and heartwarming. The world may be a diverse and complicated place, but the more experiences I had abroad, the more I realized that I could feel at home in almost any part of the world.

I am showing to Maria an ancient Mexican jug, in our Great Neck, N.Y. apartment.

In the front of the computer room at the Alumni Building, University of Arizona, which was dedicated to the memory of my late wife Virginia.

Signing an agreement to set-up the Keonjian Visiting Professorship at the University of Arizona.

Looking at the letter of the Mayor of St. Petersburg, inviting me back to visit the city again.

TEN

I had no place to live when I returned to New York after my long absence abroad; still I was happy to be on home ground, where everything was so familiar to me. Even the English language—hearing it on the street, on the radio, on television—sounded so melodic. There was no longer a need for an interpreter! I had not known how much I would miss America when I went on those assignments.

After a week I secured an apartment in Great Neck, a suburb of New York City, near enough to that big city to enjoy its cultural life without being constantly subjected to pickpockets, robberies, harassment on the streets and in the subway, and other negative urban features.

Great Neck is still a lovely village, and its quiet charm and many trees made it very attractive to me. I enjoyed decorating my apartment with the souvenirs I had brought back from India and Egypt. To travel the twenty-five miles to New York City, I either drove or took the railroad, which was very convenient—only thirty minutes to Penn Station.

After I settled down, I contacted former colleagues and secured a few consulting contracts, which kept me busy until my eventual move to a new home in Arizona.

I became an active member of the American Institute of Archaeology (AIA) and joined the organization's North Shore Branch on Long Island, where I organized an Egyptian Study Group. Its twenty-five members had all visited Egypt and were eager to share their experiences. Our weekly meetings usually involved a presentation by one of our members, followed by discussions and finally the inevitable coffee and cake. Not only were the evenings interesting and informative, but I felt like part of a family.

By the time I moved to Arizona, our AIA branch had ten different study groups, including Roman, Greek, Biblical, Meso-american, Near East, and Discovery. Once a month there was a general meeting and a presentation by invited prominent personalities.

I was also a member of the Explorers' Club, whose early leaders had included President Theodore Roosevelt, the widely traveled newscaster Lowell Thomas, and Sir Edmund Hillary, now an honorary president. With Tensing Norkay (Sherpa Tenzing), Sir Edmund was the first man to conquer the twenty-nine-thousand-foot Mount Everest. He was knighted for that 1953 achievement and became New Zealand High Commissioner to India in 1984.

The Explorers' Club held an annual banquet in the Waldorf Astoria's Grand Ballroom. Live animals such as cheetahs, eagles, camels, wolves, baboons, and others were displayed as part of the lecture presentations. After the lectures, an elaborate and diverse dinner was always served. On the menu were unusual foods from all over the world. Whole deer and steers were roasted to perfection; strange herbs and vegetables were prepared in such a delicious way that many a gourmet would have liked to obtain the recipes. Each item would be listed with the country of origin and an explanation of how the aboriginal peoples had come to adopt it as a food. Some of the menu items were strange and intriguing.

The Circumnavigators' Club, whose members traveled around the world to promote peace and international understanding, was another of my organizations. A year after I joined I was elected program chairman. The club not only hosted formal monthly presentations that concerned people and events in various parts of the world, the members also visited news organizations such as the *New York Times*.

My interests were not all so cosmopolitan. Situated among nearly a hundred theaters, concert halls, and civic buildings was a unique and very old theater called the Comedy Club. Located in the old horse stables of Sniffen Court on East Thirty-Sixth Street, the Comedy Club was, in fact, the oldest and smallest of the theaters. Its preservation had been ensured by its placement on the National Register of Historic Places.

Comedy Club actors were not professionals but amateurs that included prominent New York businessmen for whom acting had been a lifelong hobby. One such member was William Steinway, grandson of the founder of the legendary piano manufacturing company. William's father and mother had met and married at the theater.

I was happy to be accepted as a Comedy Club associate member. That status entitled me to all club privileges without being an actor. Membership dues were nearly insignificant.

With a capacity of ninety-eight, the theater allows attendance at no charge but only through the invitation of a club member. Men wear black tie, women wear formal dresses, and each event is elegant.

The theater's location and entrance from the street do not stand out among other buildings on the block. It is painted gray, and its small door has no markings except the inconspicuous house number.

Living so close to New York, I was also able to indulge the enduring love of ballet that I had carried in my heart since my years in Leningrad. Widely considered the foremost ballet choreographer of the twentieth century, Balanchine died in 1983 at the age of seventy-nine. He had been the heart and soul of the New York City Ballet Company since 1948.

The dance company Balanchine had formed in the Soviet Union utilized distinctive innovations that were frowned on by the authorities. During a foreign tour in 1924, he and another group of dancers remained in Berlin. After spending several years in Paris, Balanchine went to New York and in 1934 opened the School of American Ballet. From then on he devoted most of his career to establishing a distinctly American tradition of dance.

Balanchine choreographed Broadway shows and Hollywood musicals as well as ballet productions. Among his New York City Ballet Company presentations, his favorites were "Tzigane," Andante from

Divertimento No. 15, and *The Four Temptations* with Suzanne Farrell, Peter Martins, and Merrill Ashley. My favorite, however, was *The Prodigal Son* with Mikhail Baryshnikov, who defected from the Soviet Union in August 1974. Marie Tallchieff, who was briefly married to Balanchine, was one of my favorite dancers.

(The year of Baryshnikov's defection, Alexander Solzhenitsyn, the 1970 Nobel Prize for Literature recipient, left the Soviet Union under different circumstances: he was expelled after a brief mock trial in Moscow. Solzhenitsyn, the strongest critic of the post-Stalin era, is the author of *The Gulag Archipelago*. After the second Russian Revolution of 1990 and 1991, when communist rule was toppled—nominally— his Russian citizenship was restored, and in 1994 he returned to Russia.)

New York was also blessed with the American Ballet Theater and its classical repertoire. My cultural interests were not confined to ballet, however. I tried very hard never to miss the annual film festivals at Avery Fisher Hall at the Lincoln Center, and I attended a few Broadway and off-Broadway performances, chiefly dramas, since I had no taste for musicals.

Museums? Definitely! The Metropolitan, the Museum of Natural History (what an immense structure and what enormous collections!) and the Freek Gallery were my favorite destinations.

One evening I was invited to a private show of paintings and artifacts collected by a prominent industrialist and builder, Mr. Alan. He took me by the arm to show me one of the pieces he liked most. During our conversation I noticed his very heavy accent.

"Incidentally," I said, "what country are you from?"

He stopped and said angrily, "I am from Brooklyn. Have you heard of such a place?" He walked away, thinking I had been making fun of his Brooklyn accent, but that had not been my intention.

Once when I served as a jury foreman in the U.S. Federal Court in Brooklyn, I asked a female juror what her nationality was.

"Polish," she replied without hesitation. But when I asked her where she had been born, she answered, "In Brooklyn."

"Then you are American?" I asked.

"No, Polish," she said.

"What should I put next to her name?" I asked the judge.

"Let her be," he said. "Put 'American.'"

This was my second encounter with Brooklyn.

During the jury selection process, the lawyers on both sides, as is customary, were scrutinizing the potential jurors, forty-six of whom were eliminated and replaced with new ones. I stayed on through the whole process; somehow I appeared agreeable to both sides. Then I found out why.

The case involved the management of a foreign country versus an American labor organization, the Longshoremen's Union. The former thought that my non-American accent indicated that I would probably side with them, while the labor union interpreted my accent as meaning that I was probably a laborer, just off the boat. After the verdict was rendered in favor of the foreign country, labor union lawyers accosted me outside the courtroom, saying, "You fooled all of us."

Meanwhile, I was engaged successfully in electronics consulting work that was, at the same time, not very time-consuming. A Long Island electronics company, specializing in installing stereo systems in passenger planes, had signed a contract with the Soviet airline Aeroflot to put a system in its largest airplane, the "Illushin." The company hired me as an interpreter for a group of seven Soviet technicians who were in the U.S. for three weeks to familiarize themselves with the project and hammer out its specifications.

Of the seven, I discovered, only one had intimate knowledge of the project, but he was not the head of the group. The leader was actually a stocky, rough-looking fellow who controlled the group's every step inside and outside the conference room. Two others were clearly KGB agents, or "Nannies," with no technical knowledge. Their job was to keep an eye on the others. The function of the remaining four delegates was unclear to me. They participated only superficially in discussions, never contributing much on their own.

Our daily meetings were held at the electronics company, whose representatives attended for only the first few days. They soon became convinced not only that I was a good interpreter but that I could discuss the project's technical aspects as well. Thus I was the lone American representative in the discussions. On weekends I accompanied the group to nearby department stores so they could buy souvenirs to take home.

During the third week of discussions, the company was surprised by an unusual demand from the Soviet delegates: to run an extra wire from the cockpit to the passenger seats in addition to the regular connections that were part of the stereo system. The company was puzzled, but to me the request came as no surprise. Knowing the Soviet way of life, I had good reason to suspect that the additional wire would provide a means of monitoring the passengers' conversations.

At the end of the third week I took the Soviets to a Howard Johnson's restaurant to treat them to ice cream. "All the Howard Johnson's restaurants carry twenty-eight flavors of ice cream," I said. "Make your choice and order the one you would like to have."

They looked at the menu in silence. No one uttered a word, until the head of the group said, "Vanilla." The rest of the group quickly followed their leader, saying "vanilla" with a single voice.

"Hell," I said. "Let your leader have his vanilla if he wants, but I will order for you all different flavors." The leader would have liked to kill me, but the rest of the group was delighted, eating banana, pistachio, coffee, strawberry, peach, and chocolate ice cream.

I had remained active in the IEEE, and one year the organization's annual convention was in Boston. The preconvention cocktail party was held in the Boston Sheraton Hotel lobby, where nearly eight hundred people were uncomfortably squeezed together like sardines. Next to me was a very striking woman suffering no less than I from this most crowded situation.

I said to her, "I am glad that I am suffering in the company of such an attractive lady like you."

"Please do not talk to me like that," she retorted. "I am a married woman."

"Big deal!" I said. "If you are so afraid of your husband, we can get rid of him very fast, except I do not know how he would like to die:

with a knife, a rope, a bullet, or poison. You as his wife should know his preference."

"Why do you not ask him yourself?" she said. "He stands next to you."

I turned to face a smiling gentleman, who had heard the entire conversation, and he said, "I like you. Would you like to have dinner with us tonight?"

Always eager for a new experience, I readily accepted. Still trying to manage my drink and hors d'oeuvres on my plate, I pulled out my wallet to write his address on a piece of paper. A snapshot of Abla, my Egyptian secretary, fell to the floor.

The man picked it up and handed it to me, glancing at it and then shouting excitedly, "What is the picture of my dear sister Abla doing in your wallet?"

I explained, and he said, "Oh! Then you must be her former boss Eduardo. She wrote to me about you several times."

After dinner at his house, I wrote to Abla, who was still living in Cairo. "Guess from where I am writing this letter! From your brother's house, in Boston!"

After two weeks came her reply: "Big deal! My brother was in America, you were in America, of course you had to meet each other. It just was the will of Allah!"

On another occasion, when I was a guest at the annual Polish Ball ("Polonaise") in New York, the beautiful Princess Grace of Monaco opened the ball. At dinner, I was seated with five bachelors, and we all were admiring the princess: her carriage, her charm, her demeanor. She was truly regal, we agreed. My table partners began to tease me, betting that I would not dare to invite her to dance. I really got angry.

So I approached the princess's table and said, "Your Highness, do you see those five men at that table? They are teasing me, saying that I would not dare to invite you for a dance. Would you please help me and dance with me?"

She smiled and gracefully agreed. We danced only six minutes. Noticing the name tag on my jacket, she said, "You must be Armenian. I have a wonderful Armenian friend back in Monaco by the name of Serge Hakopian. I am sure you know him."

"Sorry, I do not," I said.

She was genuinely surprised. "How come?" she said. "I thought all Armenians knew each other. But since you do not know him," she continued, "I will have to introduce you to him. I will give a small dinner party for you next Saturday at my residence in Monaco. I hope you will come. My Armenian friend Serge will be there."

"I will be very happy to come," I replied, "but how will I find you without knowing your address and telephone number? Who knows you in Monaco?"

Hearing this she gave me a long and understanding look, smiled, and kissed me on the cheek. "I appreciated what you said. I knew that Armenians had an excellent sense of humor."

I escorted her to her table and returned to my table partners, triumphant. A few months later I heard she had been killed in an automobile accident in Monaco. I reacted as if I had lost a dear friend, although I had known her only for a delightful six minutes.

Joe Cullman 3rd, the former Chairman of the Board of Philip Morris Company, was another interesting man whom I met in New York City. I always enjoyed his charming personality and his sharp sense of humor. In fact, I was treated as a member of his extended family, which I cherished very much. In the course of our friendship, I traveled with him to Canada on a salmon fishing trip and made other trips abroad with some members of his family.

In September 1989, I attended the Explorers' Club in New York City. The auditorium was packed. The crowd had come to hear a lecture on "Ice Formations" by Dr. Igor Zotikov, a Russian scientist and famous oceanographer. Zotikov had just returned from an expedition to Antarctica, where he spent two years with his American colleagues.

Being an artist by nature, he had brought along his vivid paintings of the region, and they were displayed all over the club. I was unable to secure a place for myself in the auditorium, so I waited outside the doors, trying to catch at least part of his talk. I wanted to shake hands with the speaker and chat with him in Russian.

Professor Zotikov was of medium height and medium build. What most attracted one's attention was his "burnt by the sun" face, white beard, and vivacious eyes.

He was very much in demand and we had only a short chat. I handed him my calling card and went home. It was after midnight when the telephone rang. Professor Zotikov was on the other end.

"Do you know, Edward, that I am a relative of yours!" he said in a very animated voice. "I am the brother-in-law of your dear niece Anna, in Moscow! Could I spend an evening with you?"

In less than an hour he was in my apartment in Great Neck, Long Island. He immediately put in a telephone call to Moscow.

"Anna, you would never guess where I am calling you from! From your Uncle [*cousin* in America] Edward Keonjian's apartment! He is alive and doing well in America! This is some miraculous coincidence that we found each other under such odd circumstances!"

Because of the Iron Curtain, I had never seen my niece or my other relatives, so I was understandably excited, especially after I learned that Anna was coming to the U.S. the very next year to give a talk at Cornell University. I could not wait for a year to go by and started a very active correspondence with her.

In the meantime, Professor Zotikov returned to New York on business and brought me his latest book, published in Moscow and titled *Picnic on the Appalachian Trail*. It depicted various humorous incidents he had encountered in the U.S. during his previous visits.

Finally came the day of Anna's arrival in New York City on her way to Ithaca, New York. I waited anxiously at the JFK airport, where she was to be picked up by car by an American colleague, Dr. Margaret Egar, who would be attending the same symposium. (Later she would become a good friend of ours.)

My niece resembled her late mother, Flora, my favorite first cousin in Tiflis, Georgia. It was an emotional meeting, although very short—not more than twenty-five minutes—and we made arrangements for her to stay at my place on her way back home to Moscow.

The week we spent together was full of remembrances of my past. I learned about many of my relatives and their fates. I also found out that my parents had passed away. Anna, being the historian of the family, was able to draw our family tree and name everyone. I found myself "hanging" from one of those "branches." This is how I learned that my great-grandfather on my mother's side was a Georgian serf. It was quite a revelation!

Despite my advanced age—over seventy—I was still considered a popular available bachelor, not committed as yet to anybody. Only once I slipped and let my guard down, and I lived to regret it. My involvement with this woman was a disaster. She could not live up to my expectations, and I had all kinds of problems with her until I decided to break off our relatively short relationship. Then I became even more cautious. Still my always loving friends continued to introduce me again and again to their single female friends. And every time, for one reason or another, I would find their choice unsuitable. It always angered them. They could not understand why I did not like their choices when they liked these particular women so much. It never occurred to them that my opinion mattered and could be different from theirs. It reminded me of the story of my pretty Japanese "prospective bride."

On the other hand, when I occasionally did fall in love with someone I would find that the object of my interest had her own problems that prevented her from accepting my courtship. I was introduced to the lovely, intelligent, and well-traveled widow of the late CBS newscaster Lowell Thomas and liked her very much. The feeling was mutual, I believe, and I proposed marriage. Unfortunately she turned down my proposal, saying that her deep involvement in the lives of her four children would prevent her from giving me as much time as a wife as she would like to.

There was another bachelor in the family as well—my son, Karik, who visited me every year from Chicago. Each time he would bring with him a new girl friend, and each time I would ask, "When are you going to get married?" Each time I would receive the same answer: "Oh, Dad, I have plenty of time," although he was already past forty. It was disappointing because by now he had been a bachelor for a long time—it had been almost sixteen years since his divorce from Bobby—and I was hoping for grandchildren before it was too late.

Finally, on one annual visit he brought the woman who would become his wife. I flew to Chicago for the wedding and was so happy that I got carried away, dancing as though it were my own wedding day, until I felt a tap on my shoulder. It was my son, who, like his mother, had never been a great lover of dancing.

"Father, slow down," he said. "This is my wedding, not yours."

"Of course, of course, I understand," I said, and returned to my table. But not for long. As soon as the music resumed, I was back on my feet and danced the evening away. My son saw that it was hopeless to appeal to my common sense.

On January 18, 1983, I became a grandfather. Although little Camille looked nothing like my Armenian side of the family, I was a very happy grandfather, although I still was hoping for a grandson.

My happiness was put on hold, however, by the death of my faithful and devoted childhood friend, Serge Shahparonian, whom I had helped come to America and who had settled in Los Angeles. Just a few days before his death, he telephoned me from his sickbed, saying, "Edward, come over; you are the only one who can save my life." Poor Serge; he was confident of my ability to surmount all odds. I later learned that he had an incurable tumor in his brain, and I recalled that for as long as I could remember, even from our school years, he had complained of headaches. After washing his hair he always wore a turban and would not go outdoors for a whole day.

By the time I arrived in Los Angeles it was already too late. His desperate plea for help was a *deja vu* experience, reminding me of Virginia's similar plea from her deathbed: "Edward, I am dying; you are the only one who can save me."

Even so, she always doubted in my ability to do anything right.

When I would receive a promotion or other professional success, she would say, "Why *you*? Who are you? Why do they consider you to be better than anybody else?" Still she enjoyed the limelight of my success, traveling all around the world with me and being showered with attention and gifts. Her perennial lack of confidence in me always annoyed me. Obviously it reflected her own lack of confidence in herself.

Once in New York I was the guest of honor at a dinner party given by the widow of a distinguished diplomat. Around the dinner table in her spacious Park Avenue apartment, the conversation shifted to Russia. The guests spoke of their experiences visiting Russia in various capacities and also praised some Russian refugees in America who had struggled to succeed.

"I too have had experience with Russian refugees," our hostess commented. "I employed a Russian as a cleaning woman. She tried very hard to do her job as well as she could, but I could see that she was not used to it. After four months she left me without even picking up her last paycheck. I never heard from her again, and I wondered what ever happened to her. Maybe you, Edward, had a chance to meet her."

"What was her name?" I asked. "Was it Virginia?"

"Yes, it was," said my hostess. "Do you know where she is now?"

"She passed away a long time ago," I answered.

"How do you know for sure?"

"She was my wife."

For a few minutes a very uncomfortable silence descended on the guests.

Because of professional success and my publications in the U.S., I was always an object of curiosity among my former colleagues from the Soviet Union who would come to New York to attend international electronics conferences. They would seek me out and ask me questions about various aspects of life in this country and about how I was able to succeed. My popularity was a constant source of irritation to the Soviet officials accompanying the delegates; they believed that it could lead to defection. So they resorted to a character assassination of Virginia. An article in *Isvestia* (the official Soviet newspaper) painted her as a temptress who used her charms to lure Soviet delegates to the West. The article was faithfully reprinted in American and foreign newspapers.

A month later, at the annual banquet of the IEEE (Institute of Electrical and Electronic Engineers) in New York, Virginia and I were seated at the table of the Soviet delegates as interpreters. The delegates had read the *Isvestia* article and were stiff in their conversation with us. Near the end of the banquet, a dozen or so high U.S. military officials, all of whom had read the article and knew me personally, lined up in front of Virginia and with great zest, loudly enough so that those seated around the table could hear, exclaimed, "Dear Virginia, what terrific news we read in the newspapers—that you are such a wonderful seducer of innocent men! Could we have an appointment with you?"

I translated every word of this charade to the Soviets. They were stunned in disbelief! Only one of them uttered, "What a strange humor these Americans have!"

Another occasion where I served as an interpreter was at a private party attended by eight well-known Soviet scientists. The party proceeded merrily. People told nonpolitical jokes and the Soviets made references to how attached Americans are to their automobiles—how they take their vehicles wherever they go, even to the moon!

Shortly after the Soviets left the party, one of the American guests discovered that her fur coat was missing. We telephoned the head of the Soviet delegation at the hotel and told him what had happened. "Don't worry," he said. "I know who did it. You will get the coat immediately."

The coat was returned and everyone was happy. Strangely, nobody really expressed outrage at so inappropriate an incident—so unfitted to scientists of their caliber.

Several years later, I received an invitation to address the Popov Society in Moscow in connection with its fortieth anniversary. The Popov Society, equivalent to our IEEE, was a branch of the Soviet National Academy of Science. By then one of my books had been translated into Russian and I was well known among Soviet scientists and engineers working in my field of microelectronics, even though my name had been carefully omitted from the Russian editions. ("It's just an oversight," officials visiting New York would tell me.)

With the invitation in my hand, I contacted the U.S. State Department and asked if it would be safe for me to go to Moscow.

"It's pretty safe," I was told. "You are an American citizen now."

"But suppose the Soviets would hold me back and prevent me from returning to the U.S.A.?" I asked. "How would you protect me in that case? Could you do anything about it?"

"Nothing," the State Department official said. "According to their laws you are still a Soviet citizen. Therefore, formally, we can't do anything to protect you."

"But I am an American citizen now," I persisted. "Why can't I rely on your protection?"

"Very simple," the man said. "Do you think that we can jeopardize our relations with the Soviets because of one single individual? Be realistic. If you have any doubts regarding this trip, just do not go."

It put a good chill on me for the rest of my life.

In earlier years, when Virginia was still alive, the head of the Popov Society had visited me every time he was in New York. Professor S. I. Siforov had been my professor at the Leningrad Electrotechnical Institute, and obviously the KGB had instructed him to "pick my brain." In reality, we never had any technical discussions, and the only thing he wanted from us was Virginia's help in choosing some necessities for his family in Moscow.

During one of these visits, following KGB instructions, he unexpectedly began trying to pressure us to visit Russia, to "see with our own eyes" how everything had changed there for the better. It was too much for my fiery Virginia. Ignoring the fact that he was, after all, our guest, she shouted, "How can we believe your words—that yesterday's murderers of millions of innocent people became suddenly angels? To me, you, the Soviets, are all liars and murderers." Nothing could calm her down, not even my kicking her gently under the table. Our guest sat silently, not able to utter a word. Later, when I was driving him to his hotel, he said, "Edward, you are so lucky to have such a smart wife. I just envy you."

By the time of Karik's remarriage, Virginia had been gone for many years. In my late seventies, I still felt like a middle-aged man. Time had passed so quickly. That is why I was taken aback by an incident, when I was 79, on a bus in New York.

The bus was overcrowded and I was standing, holding onto the strap, when I heard a young girl say, "Mister, would you like my seat?" I did not interpret it as a sign of respect. Did I look so old that people were willing to give me their seats on buses?

When I arrived home I took a look at myself in the mirror. The girl had been right. The face of a well-seasoned senior citizen was looking at me from the mirror. Where had the years gone? Although it took a while, I learned not to be bothered by that senior citizen's seasoned face. I just got used to it, I guess.

Still I was eager to travel. I had become intrigued by the state of affairs in South Africa, and I decided to go and see this apartheid police state.

I found a partner to travel with, Nan Boas. It was a long trip, more than seventeen hours, with a stopover in the Verdi Islands. We finally reached Johannesburg and spent a few days in this prosperous and vibrant city before traveling to Pretoria, the original stronghold of the Boers and now the administrative capital of South Africa. Then we flew to Durban, a town with a predominantly Indian population on the shores of the Indian Ocean.

Although Portuguese explorers reached the Cape of Good Hope in the late 1400s, it was the Dutch who in 1652 began to settle in what is now the Republic of South Africa. The area's original inhabitants were Khoisan tribespeople; in the eleventh century Bantu tribes migrated there from the north.

The original Dutch colony was founded by Jan van Riebeek, who organized a group of farms at Cape Town to raise food for vessels of the Netherlands East India Company. Dutch and French Huguenot settlers formed a colony there that was seized by the British in 1806.

After decades of tension between the slaveholding Dutch "Boers" and the English settlers, Great Britain abolished slavery throughout the Empire in 1833. Three years later the Boers, with their families, wagons, and cattle, began the Great Trek northward, settling in the Orange Free State, Natal, and the Transvaal Republic. Hostility continued, however, and was exacerbated by the discovery of gold and diamonds.

(The Englishman Cecil John Rhodes at one time controlled the country's diamond mines. He became prime minister of Cape Colony in 1890. After he died in 1902, his fortunes endowed scholarships for American, German, and British "Rhodes Scholars" at Oxford University.)

Paul Kruger, who took part in the Great Trek, became the leader of the Boer independence movement. He was head of the provisional government in the first Boer War and in 1883 became president of the South African Republic. Despite his efforts to seek European alliances against Britain, the British eventually triumphed in the South African Wars, and Transvaal, Natal, the Orange Free State, and Cape Province were joined as the Union of South Africa, a dominion of the British Empire, in 1910. Fifty years later the country became an independent republic, by this time suffering from racial unrest motivated by the policy of apartheid. Under apartheid, blacks and coloreds (people of mixed race) were required to carry a number of passes and indentification papers, their movement was restricted, their education was separate and unequal, and they were subjected to any number of other constraints and indignities. It would not be until 1990 that President de Klerk would begin to dismantle the apartheid system, paving the way for the vast black majority to choose one of their own, longtime activist Nelson Mandela, as the country's leader. But this liberation was yet to occur at the time of my visit, and apartheid was very much in evidence.

Although Johannesburg is the largest city in South Africa, the country's administrative capital is Pretoria, its judicial capital Bloemfontein, and its legislative capital Cape Town.

While we were still in Johannesburg, I was visiting in the home of a British artist and her husband, who lived in a very grand house. To my surprise, I saw on their bookshelves many books on Communism and the Soviet Union. Even more surprising were the portraits of Communist leaders on the walls and various Russian texts on the table.

"Why do you study Russian?" I asked.

"Because," they answered, "the Soviet Union is the most progressive country in the world. Sooner or later it will liberate South Africa from the apartheid system, and the Russian language will be very handy to use with the Soviet representatives who will be installed in this country. Many of our friends study Russian."

I saw that I wanted nothing to do with people who thought this way, and I quickly headed for the exit with a bad taste in my mouth.

From Durban we flew to Elizabeth, a large and busy port through which passed South Africa's many exports: sugar, wine, asbestos, copper, gold (more than half the world's supply), uranium, platinum, chromite ore, iron ore, diamonds, and much more from this small but remarkably industrious country, which is able to supply electricity to almost all of Africa.

There are large ostrich farms all over, and I visited one of them, where tens of thousands of ostriches roamed, always in pairs. I was told that when the female partner dies her mate will never pair with another female, but if the male partner dies the female finds a mate almost instantly.

Ostrich eggs are huge, up to twenty times larger than chicken eggs, and they are very sturdy, with thick shells. I know that for a fact because, as heavy as I am, when I stepped on one of them it did not crack. At lunch about twenty of my fellow travelers and I were served an omelet made from "a single ostrich egg." It tasted exactly like one made of chicken eggs.

I spent three days at a private wild-animal preserve, Sabi-Sabi, somewhat smaller than the well-known Kruger National Park but with fewer tourists and greater access to the animals. Very early every morning, the warden would take us to the area where the elephants, antelopes, zebras, wildebeests, giraffes, hippopotomuses, and other animals can be most closely observed, sometimes from as little as seven feet away. The warden would sit on the hood of the Jeep, his rifle ready if the animals threatened us. The same procedure would be repeated in the evening, when the animals came to the water hole. It was especially exciting at night, when the Jeep's lights would allow us to come very close to the animals, almost too close to be believed.

We took the Garden Route from Elizabeth to Cape Town, a good three days' journey. We stopped in the town of Stollenbock, home of the university of the same name and gateway to the wine country. More than a hundred excellent wines are produced by descendants of French Hughenots who came to these shores.

In beautiful Cape Town, two things in particular drew my attention. One was a long line of students in front of Howard College waiting to enroll. Under the influence of what I had read in the American media, I was amazed to see that this line was racially mixed—whites, coloreds, and blacks standing next to each other, chatting joyously. Likewise, in the huge, ultramodern, six-story department store, the clerks were white as well as black and the customers were largely black. I was surprised to see that so many blacks were able to buy goods in that expensive store. The same surprise awaited me in a fashionable restaurant, where the tables were occupied by blacks as well as whites.

In other areas, however, apartheid was conspicuous. It was on the beaches, in the trains and buses, in housing and schools. I learned more about apartheid when I began visiting black neighborhoods. As I write these lines, I am happy to be able to say that apartheid in South Africa is a thing of the past.

When I was a child, looking at the map of South Africa, I dreamed of one day being on the tip of the Cape of Good Hope. It is on Cape Peninsula, thirty miles south of Cape Town, on a promontory two hundred fifty feet high and a hundred feet wide, where the Indian and the Atlantic oceans merge. My dream had been to put one foot in one ocean and the other foot in the other ocean. When I finally found myself at that place, I saw how hopeless it was to fulfill my childhood desire. The two oceans at that point confront each other with such a violent fracas that it was out of the question to even attempt to approach the place where they meet.

Soon after my return from South Africa I observed an interesting phenomenon. I was attending a professional conference in Cambridge, Massachusetts. During lunch I sat with two couples. I mentioned that I had recently returned from South Africa and that the trip had been an eye-opener for me. Upon hearing this, the two couples left immediately without finishing their meals. What an example of the power of propaganda. "Do not give me any facts," their behavior seemed to say. "My mind is already made up!" I have had similar experiences abroad when I made favorable comments about life in the United States. How sad that some people are so incurious, not wanting to learn what they do not know.

Still driven from childhood by the long-suppressed thirst to travel, and still being in good health, I also decided to visit the South Pacific, Bora Bora, and other islands. Bora Bora is a picturesque volcanic island, one of the Society Islands of French Polynesia. Its large lagoon is crowned with coral islets. I had heard tales that on Bora Bora one can still see the Sirens, mythological sea nymphs whose singing was said to draw sailors to the shores of their island. So on one long voyage, as we were returning to the States, I made a stopover in the hope of seeing at least one of them. I saw many, but they all were without fins.

I had also long been curious about the unique culture of the Maoris, so I decided to visit New Zealand, gain first-hand information, and return to New York with photographs for my Discovery archaeological group on Long Island.

Now representing less than ten percent of New Zealand's population, the Maoris were the island nation's first inhabitants. They probably arrived about 800 A.D., having made the voyage in long canoes from the distant Marquesas, like the Society Islands a part of what is now French Polynesia. They settled in a place called Rotorua, in the land of hot geysers.

By 1800 there were more than a hundred thousand Maoris in

New Zealand, but in the nineteenth century they came to be outnumbered by European *(paheka)* settlers. Their culture declined, they lost most of their land, and by the end of the century their population had shrunk to about forty thousand. Since the 1970s, however, they have become politically more assertive. The population has again risen to nearly three hundred thousand. The Maori language is officially encouraged, and they have regained some of their land. I stayed in the center of the region in a small cottage, where I had my own hot sulfur jacuzzi right at my bedroom door. It was surrounded with bushes for complete privacy.

A few days later I checked into another hotel in the city of Auckland, which is prized by travelers not only for proximity to the Maori region, hot springs, and trout fishing, but for the stalactite caves at nearby Waitomo which are lit by thousands of glowworms.

The next morning I noticed a commotion near my room and discovered that President Jimmy Carter and his wife, Rosalynn, were staying at the same hotel. The place was surrounded by an entourage, including Secret Service agents, that is inevitable when someone of his stature travels.

The Carters were in New Zealand on a fishing trip. I had a chance to enjoy a pleasant chat with them, and I was surprised at how personable and charming they were. My impression was quite different than it had been when I had seen them only on television.

I visited Wellington, the country's capital, then crossed Cook Strait for South Island. Traveling south, I came to the conclusion that there are more sheep than people in New Zealand. (Actually, there are more than ten sheep for each person.) The Canterbury Plains, near Christchurch, are world-famous for their mutton and lamb. In fact, some seventy percent of the occupied land in New Zealand is devoted to supporting livestock.

Christchurch seemed more British than any town in England in its character, architecture, food, and other attributes. The main attraction was "the Archwizard of Canterbury," who would perch on a small pedestal and talk and talk on various human virtues to a small group of listeners. I was told that he had no nationality, no ID papers, yet everyone knew him. Once he had to go to Australia but, not having any papers, he was not permitted to travel. Finally, the authorities decided to treat him as a living work of art, and they shipped him to Australia in a sort of wooden crate with no name attached to it. So say the townspeople in Christchurch.

In a small gallery in Christchurch I saw a poster depicting a "derriere" clad in very suggestive black panties, a garter belt, and, of course, black stockings. On the bottom of the poster in small letters were the names of the photographer and the model. They were from a place well known to me: Sea Cliff, Long Island, New York, thirteen thousand miles away. It's a small world!

I found South Island more picturesque than North Island, with its fjords, fantastic scenery, and Mount Cook, at more than twelve thousand feet the highest peak in the Southern Alps.

New Zealanders, who have nicknamed themselves Kiwis after the flightless bird of their land, are a friendly people. Their love for their beautiful country is contagious, and my visit there was a delight.

Vacationing in Jamaica one spring, I made the acquaintance of a British couple in a remote area of the island. They were putting the finishing touches on a translation from Italian to English of the "biography" of Leonardo Da Vinci. The "biography" had supposedly been "discovered" only recently and described the famous artist's early years as an apprentice in a restaurant. The material was fictitious, of course, full of humor and hyperbole.

I thought the story would be appropriate for a presentation, all in jest, at my Great Neck Archaeological Group. I persuaded the couple to give me a copy of the book's galleys, and they agreed under the condition that I would not introduce any of it in print or any other form before publication.

The galleys were voluminous and full of illustrations. It was too much for one speaker to handle, so I distributed the material among twenty-two members of the group, who would present their parts in sequence. All presentations would be illustrated with slides. The program was a resounding success, and its format was adopted for future lectures.

As time passed, and I was not getting any younger, I decided to make two more trips abroad to places I had not been before. I joined a tour organized by the Museum of Natural History to visit the prehistoric caves of Lascaux and other caves in the Perigord Region of southern France. Seeing the life-size, full-color paintings made twenty thousand years ago on the cave walls by ancient people was mind-boggling.

One day my son called me and said that I should not miss the fantastic voyage around the world available through wonderful Singapore Airlines. Since I had never seen Formosa Island, Sri Lanka, or Singapore, I decided to include them in my itinerary. I bought a ticket without reserving accommodations on any leg of the trip, which I lived to regret. Still, I made enough pictures and accumulated enough information to give six different presentations to my Asian group of the AIA.

At the end of 1982, while I was still grieving the loss of my dear friend Serge, my life took a different turn. One Sunday I was invited to attend a church service at the Russian Orthodox Church in Sea Cliff. After the service I met an Armenian of about my age, Mikael, and his beautiful wife, Maria. She was so different from other women I had met that I could hardly take my eyes off her.

Soon after, the couple invited me to their home for a Christmas party, and I had a chance to learn more about Maria. She had been born in Paris and had immigrated to the United States with her family when she was seventeen. In 1957, when she was twenty-three, she had married Mikael. Their two children were by this time grown and had left home.

About six months later I was planning a party at my home, and I asked Maria and her husband to help me with the arrangements, which they gladly agreed to. At the party were four of my female friends, who invariably viewed me as a potential husband. I was unable to conceal my admiration of Maria, and apparently it was obvious not only to the four women but to Mikael. As a result, Maria and her husband never again invited me to their home, and I lost my female friends as well. This is life!

Within a year I learned that Maria and Mikael were divorced. I was surprised, since there had been no sign of unhappiness between them. Much later I learned that after their children had left home the relationship between them had begun to deteriorate.

I started seeing Maria frequently, and eventually we got married. It was a meeting of hearts and the happiest time in many long years of loneliness.

For our honeymoon we went to the Canary Islands for two weeks. The name of this Spanish archipelago off the northwest coast of Africa has nothing to do with small yellow birds but rather refers to the many dogs (Latin *canis*) once found on Gran Canaria.

The islands are seventy-five miles off the African Western Sahara. We stayed on the island of Tenerife, the largest of the seven islands. Its splendid scenery and mild subtropical climate make it a favorite tourist resort. We were treated to spectacular shows in a very unusual night club situated under the laguna. Spain sends its best artists and dancers to Puerto de la Cruz, an island town greatly favored by the Spanish kings of old.

Two years later Maria and I repeated our "honeymoon," this time in Sicily. The largest and most populous island in the Mediterranean Sea, Sicily is separated from the Italian mainland by the narrow Strait of Messina, only two kilometers wide.

From my archaeological viewpoint, the trip was a bonanza. Many cultures have left their mark on this island: Greeks, Romans, Carthaginians, Vandals, Normans, Arabs, and many others. I was glad to be there with Maria to share my impressions with her on the spot. She is my sister soul.

Situated in the middle of the Mediterranean Sea between Africa and Europe, the island has historically been a battlefield for the continents. Its early settlers, probably related to those in southern Italy, were conquered by the Greeks, who founded the colonies of Syracuse, Agrigentum, Naxos, and others. The Greek temples on the island are so numerous and magnificent that when Maria and I presented a lecture on Sicily at one of the AIA meetings we justifiably called it "If You Want to See Greece Go to Sicily."

In the meantime, President Ronald Reagan's announcement that the U.S. would commit itself to the Star Wars project had catastrophic consequences in Russia and, in fact, for the Communist Party. Russia's economy was already falling behind those of most industrialized countries. Now, trying to catch up with the U.S., Russia committed all its resources to develop its own "Star Wars" project and found itself unable to do so. In that process, the Russian economy came to the brink of disaster.

The new general secretary of the Russian Communist Party, M. Gorbachev, was one of the ablest and shrewdest members of the all-powerful Politburo. He tried to save the situation and his own leading position by introducing the now-famous slogans *"Perestroika"* (restructuring the economy) and *"glasnost"* (openness, a sort of freedom of expression). He ended the disastrous Russian war in Afghanistan and sanctioned the end of the communist monopoly in eastern Europe. For his efforts he received the Nobel Peace Prize in 1990.

Glasnost and *perestroika* were not popular with the Soviet people. While Gorbachev became president of the USSR, his measures did not bring a significant improvement in the economy. About *perestroika*, people claimed there were two possible ways it could succeed, "one realistic and the other pure fantasy. The *realistic* possibility is that extraterrestrials would land in a space ship and help us. The *fantasy* is that we will help ourselves."

Glasnost and *perestroika* scared the high communist officials, the managers of the industrial centers, who were deeply entrenched in the system. These hard-liners tried to unseat Gorbachev. They failed, yet Gorbachev eventually had to resign. It was, in effect, the end of communist dictatorship in Russia.

After our marriage, Maria had moved to my apartment in Great Neck and begun sharing many of my interests and activities in New York City. She was an excellent life companion for me—always enthusiastic, always genuinely interested in science, politics, travel, history, and so many other aspects of life. Add to that her passion for cooking, and what else can you ask for to keep a husband happy?

Unfortunately, as time passed, we both developed various kinds of arthritis and we decided to move to Arizona, where the dry climate would be more agreeable to our aching bones. In February 1993 we sold or gave away whatever furniture and household items we could not take with us, loaded our car to the brim, and drove to Arizona. In six days we reached Green Valley, population twenty thousand, located twenty-five miles south of Tucson. We did not know anybody there, but we liked it so much that we decided to settle there for good.

When our friends in the East ask why we chose Green Valley to settle in, I tell this story:

An elderly couple living in Minnesota saw an ad that had been placed by the Green Valley Chamber of Commerce. In it they read, "Green Valley is the place where nobody dies." They were so taken by this that they decided to sell their house and furniture, get in their car, and drive to their Shangri-la. They traveled for six days and finally came to the outskirts of Green Valley.

The couple's enthusiasm was quickly dimmed by the sight of a funeral procession. They decided to ignore it, thinking that perhaps it was just an anomaly. Reaching the middle of town, however, they saw another funeral procession. It was too much for them. They stormed the Chamber of Commerce, saying, "How could you advertise that nobody dies here? We have already seen two funeral processions with our own eyes."

"Please calm down," the Chamber of Commerce official said. "Everything is okay. Nobody dies in Green Valley, as we said."

"But how about those two funeral processions we just saw?" continued the couple in indignation.

"Oh, those!" said the man. "They were for the two remaining morticians, who starved to death."

We regretted that we had to leave behind our dear friends, the Milians: the vivacious Juliette; her "Romeo " Harry; and their two beautiful and talented daughters, Janette and Lara. The good-bys were tearful and emotional—they were as a family to us, but we reassured them that Arizona is not on the moon: just five hours away by jet.

Green Valley is a well-organized village of citizens over fifty-five, with excellent recreational facilities and nearly a hundred social clubs. I took an active part in the social life of Green Valley, joining its Camera Club and Toastmasters International. In June 1995, I was elected president of the Tri-State Club (the three states being New York, New Jersey, and Pennsylvania).

Once at a dinner party I was seated in the company of eight people. The head chair was empty. I asked whom we were waiting for.

"A prominent Russian scientist visiting Green Valley," I was told. But the scientist did not show up, and we started dinner without him. Out of curiosity I looked at his place card. It read, "Dr. Edward Keonjian." We completed our dinner, with the chair of the Russian scientist remaining unoccupied!

I was most favorably impressed with the University of Arizona in Tucson. Its vibrant academic life, led by a faculty that is making many valuable contributions to science and technology, inspired me to make an endowment. I established the "Edward Keonjian Visiting Professorship" in my life work, microelectronics. The endowment makes possible the annual visit of one or two scientists from this country and abroad to teach and conduct research in microelectronics at the University.

We have never regretted our move to Arizona. In fact, often we think we wasted precious years back in the East and should have made the move a long time ago. We could not have done so, not only because of the Milians, but also because our best friends, Tanya and Paul Petroff, were stricken with cancer and needed our presence while still alive.

Before our move to Arizona, we were parishioners of the newly built Armenian Church of St. Sarkis in Douglaston, Long Island, twenty miles from Manhattan. Fire had destroyed the previous church, and the new one was also built in the traditional Armenian style, typical of Armenian churches since the fourth century. In the front of the building twelve steps lead to the church entrance. On the right side there is a beautiful ten-foot-high stained-glass window with a large Armenian cross in the middle. When the sun passes through the window panes, it illuminates the area with hundreds of colors. Under the window is a small plaque bearing these words:

"In memory of Clara Holmquist"

In a world where the cruelty of human beings can be too painful to comprehend, there are those who rise above the limitations of humanity, giving mercy and compassion. Clara was my angel of mercy.

EPILOGUE

*H*ad I met someone with the same or very similar experiences related in this narrative, I would have encouraged him or her to write a book. Thus, it was quite logical to follow my own advice.

What did I want to accomplish with this story?

Well, there is the innate desire to chronicle one's life, and to put into some order random and disparate events. In my case, experiences often took place against the background of significant world events, and I do wish to make a small contribution to the history of those times.

I also hope that my story pays tribute to a whole generation of immigrants who managed to escape a hell on Earth to start life anew in the West. The more we know about the human side of what took place in Europe during the mid-twentieth century, the more we can value— and practice—what we enjoy in this country.

Finally, I want to leave the reader with this thought, born from my experiences: If one person can triumph over seemingly hopeless odds, does that not validate the idea that one should never, never give up on one's dreams?

Perhaps someday my descendants will learn a little about a man they never knew.

That alone is reason for this book.

Edward Keonjian
1996

APPENDIX

Professional Publications

Books

1970, *Air and Spaceborne Computers* (ed.), Technivision Services Publication, Slough, England

1968, *Application of Microelectronics to Aerospace Equipment* (ed., with R. C. Davy), United Kingdom

1964, *Micropower Electronics* (ed.), a Pergamon Press Book, published by the Macmillan Co., New York

1963, *Microelectronics: Theory, Design, and Fabrication* (ed.), McGraw-Hill Book Co., New York, Toronto, London; translated into six foreign languages

1957, *Transistor Circuit Engineering* (co-author), John Wiley and Sons, Inc., New York

1953, *Principles of Transistor Circuits* (co-author), John Wiley and Sons, Inc., New York; translated into six foreign languages

Other Professional Publications

1975, "Solid State Technology as Challenge to the Educational Institutions," the UNESCO Conference, Cairo, Egypt, November 17-20, 1975

1969, "Microelectronics in Space Environment," presented at the Eighth International Symposium on Space Technology and Science, Tokyo, Japan

1967, "Microelectronics in Perspective," keynote address at the WESCON Symposium, Microelectronics Comes of Age, San Francisco, California, August 23, 1967

1966, "Challenge of Microelectronics," Massachusetts Institute of Technology, Cambridge, Massachusetts, IEEE Lecture Series, October 11-December 6, 1966

1964, "Microminiaturization Begins to Grow," Pergamon Press, Ltd., London, England

1963, "Microelectronics: Yesterday, Today, and Tomorrow," Grumman Corporation internal publication

1962, "The Arma Microcomputer for Space Application" (with J. Marx), presented at the Spaceborne Computer Engineering Conference, Anaheim, California, October 30-31, 1962

1960, "Microminiature Computer Full Adder," presented at the AIEE Conference, Garden City, New York, Paper CP, 60-364

1960, "Microminiaturizing a Space Vehicle Computer," *Electronics* magazine, April 29, 1960

1959, "Fundamentals of Multivibrators" (with William Persley), *Control Engineering*, McGraw-Hill Publishing Co., Inc.

1959, "Design of a Semiconductor Solid Circuit Adder" (with J. S. Kilby of Texas Instruments), presented at the International Electron Devices Meeting, Washington, D.C., October 29-31, 1959; noted as "the most significant of three papers presented on Integrated Circuits."

1959, "Microminiaturization of Space Computer," presented at the American Rocket Society Annual Meeting, Sheraton Park Hotel, Washington, D.C., November 16-20, 1959

1959, "Microminiature Electronic Circuitry for Space Guidance," presented at the IRE WESCON Conference, San Francisco, California

1958, "Ring-Modulator Reads Low-Level DC" (with J. S. Schmidt), Electronic Industries, Philadelphia, Pa., April 1958

1957, "Unijunction Transistor Forms Flip-Flop" (with J. J. Suran), *Electronics* magazine, September 1, 1957

1957, "Low-Level DC-AC Conversion" (with J. Schmidt), presented at the AIEE Meeting, Pittsfield, Mass., April 11, 1957; Paper No. DP, 57-536

1957, "Transistorized Special Purpose Computer" (with J. Schmidt and H. Putschi), an internal General Electric Company publication

1956, "Stable Transistor Oscillator," IRE Transactions of the Professional Group on Circuit Theory, March 1956

1956, "Micro-Power Operation of Silicon Transistors," Tele-Tech and Electronic Industries, May 1956

1956, "Micropower Audio Amplifier," IRE Transactions of the Professional Group on Circuit Theory, March 1956

1955, "A Semiconductor Diode Multi-Vibrator" (with J. J. Suran), Proceedings of the IRE, July 1955

1954, "Temperature-Compensated DC Transistor Amplifier," Proceedings of the IRE, April 1954

1954, "Shaping the Characteristics of Temperature-Sensitive Elements" (with J. S. Schaffner), AIEE Summer and Pacific General Meeting, Los Angeles, California, June 21-25, 1954

1953, "D-C Amplifier Employing Junction-Type Transistors," AIEE Summer General Meeting, Atlantic City, New Jersey, June 15-19, 1953

1953, "Noise in Transistor Amplifiers" (with J. S. Schaffner), *Electronics* magazine, February 1953

1952, "An Experimental Investigation of Transistor Noise" (with J. S. Schaffner), Proceedings of the IRE, November 1952

Some U.S. Patents Granted to Dr. E. Keonjian

Patent number

2,983,863	Constant voltage source, May 10, 1961
2,876,297	Direct-coupled amplifier, March 1959
2,863,955	Direct-coupled amplifier, December 1958
2,863,008	Stabilized amplifier, December 1958
2,848,564	Temperature stabilized transistor amplifier, August 1958
2,823,372	Semiconductor network, February 1958
2,801,340	Semiconductor wave generator, July 1957
2,774,375	Wave generator network, December 1956
2,760,070	Amplifier stabilized transistor oscillator, August 1956